D1211973

# The Universal Man

## *Smithsonian History of Aviation Series*

*Von Hardesty, Series Editor*

On December 17, 1903, on a windy beach in North Carolina, aviation became a reality. The development of aviation over the course of little more than three-quarters of a century stands as an awe-inspiring accomplishment in both a civilian and military context. The airplane has brought whole continents closer together: at the same time it has been a lethal instrument of war.

This series of books is intended to contribute to the overall understanding of the history of aviation—its science and technology as well as the social, cultural, and political environment in which it developed and matured. Some publications help fill the many gaps that still exist in the literature of flight; others add new information and interpretation to current knowledge. While the series appeals to a broad audience of general readers and specialists in the field, its hallmark is strong scholarly content.

The series is international in scope and includes works in three major categories:

SMITHSONIAN STUDIES IN AVIATION HISTORY: *works that provide new and original knowledge.*

CLASSICS OF AVIATION HISTORY: *carefully selected out-of-print works that are considered essential scholarship.*

CONTRIBUTIONS TO AVIATION HISTORY: *previously unpublished documents, reports, symposia, and other materials.*

# The Universal Man

## Theodore von Kármán's Life in Aeronautics

MICHAEL H. GORN

SMITHSONIAN INSTITUTION PRESS
WASHINGTON AND LONDON

All photographs, unless otherwise indicated, are from the archives of the California Institute of Technology.


This book was edited by Initial Cap Editorial Services.

The paper used in this publication meets the minimum requirements of the American National Standard for Permanence of Paper for Printed Library Materials Z39.48-1984.

**Library of Congress Cataloging-in-Publication Data**
Gorn, Michael H.
The universal man: Theodore von Kármán's life in aeronautics / Michael H. Gorn.
p. cm.—(Smithsonian history of aviation series)
Includes bibliographical references and index.
ISBN 1-56098-165-2
1. Von Kármán, Theodore, 1881–1963. 2. Aeronautical engineers—United States—Biography. I. Title. II. Series.
TL540.V67G67 1992
629.13'0092—dc20
[B] 91-5099
CIP

Printed in the United States of America
10 9 8 7 6 5 4 3 2 1 99 98 97 96 95 94 93 92


Publisher's note: The descriptions of otherwise undocumented personal incidents and the recollections of episodes and persons are entirely the author's. Every effort has been made to verify details and insure correctness; inaccuracy if it occurs is regretted.

Cover: A familiar sight to the 'Kármán Circus'—the Boss in his study, wearing a robe. From the 1950s.

To Annette,

for believing in me,

and in fond memory of

Victor A. Klein

and

Eckford Sakaguchi

Dr. Theodore von Kármán, the Universal Man of Aeronautics. Photographed in the early 1960s. (*Source:* USAF photograph)

# Contents

# Preface

This biography recounts the career of one of the world's most eminent scientists of flight. His range of activity spanned many decades and every continent, a broad intellectual field and great institutional diversity. Like no other, he became the "universal man" of aeronautics. During a long and notably energetic life, this Hungarian-born mathematician and physicist discovered some of the fundamental laws of aerodynamics. Yet, not just content to know in an abstract sense, Theodore von Kármán applied these insights to the practical business of designing aircraft, dirigibles, rockets, and missiles. In essence, he pioneered aerospace engineering.

But Kármán's reputation rested not only on the equations for which he became famous. Equally vital were the actions he took to catalyze the disciplines of aeronautics and astronautics. Teaching played an important part. Thousands of students attended Kármán's remarkable lectures and hundreds apprenticed themselves to him. Through them, his novel approach to problem solving—as well as his research interests—have been transmitted from generation to generation. Perhaps even more important, Kármán's legacy entails the forging of institutions. He nurtured two of the world's foremost aeronautical institutes, started an organization in the front ranks of rocketry and space exploration, and founded a corporation still in the forefront of aerospace manufacturing. For the U.S. Air Force, he assembled a permanent board of scientific advisers and spurred the establishment of a separate command for air power research and development. In addition, Kármán acted for forty years on the international stage, introducing a committee of aeronautical experts to the deliberations of the North Atlantic Treaty Organization and convening regular international congresses on fluid mechanics, applied mathematics, and rocketry. In large part, Kármán's institutional creations have thrived because of his personality. Expressive and fun-loving, he was thought of not only with respect, but with affection. Clearly, he possessed a peculiar gift for harmonizing diverse talents toward a common end.

Beyond the scope of this book is his life as a consultant. Kármán propagated his ideas not only in lectures, papers, and organizations, but through countless part-time assignments. For example, he worked closely with Jack Northrop in the 1930s on early flying wing aircraft. The Los Angeles County Water District persuaded him to design high-efficiency pumps to draw inland water to the thirsty metropolis. A federal commission asked him to investigate the collapse of the Tacoma Narrows Bridge into Puget Sound. He also advised the U.S. Air Force on establishing a huge national wind tunnel complex in Tennessee and on the feasibility of aircraft flying faster than the speed of sound. Although important, such undertakings could not be treated in a book this size. Its small scale also prohibited lengthy descriptions of Kármán's scientific breakthroughs. Despite such limitations, the essence of a fascinating life remains.

All this bears on the book's intended audience: the general reader of history with a particular interest in biography, science, aeronautics, aviation, air power, rocketry, or space. In short, it is a compact study of an ingenious, pivotal, and dynamic personality. It could have been written to touch lightly on all aspects of his career, or organized to isolate the main currents and describe them in greater depth. I chose the second method, and the resulting deficiencies—indeed, all the shortcomings—are my own responsibility.

On the other hand, many people are responsible for whatever is worthwhile in this book. Through Dr. Nick Komons, retired chief historian of the Federal Aviation Administration, I became aware of the Smithsonian History of Aviation Series. Thanks to him I was introduced to the biographies editor, Prof. William Leary, who acquainted me with Felix Lowe, the director of the Smithsonian Institution Press. I owe all three men a heavy debt of gratitude, as I do the anonymous historians chosen by the publisher to review the manuscript. I am no less thankful to copyeditor Therese Boyd, a wonderful collaborator. Her clever pen not only saved me from many embarrassing gaffes, but greatly improved otherwise pedestrian prose.

Singular, too, were the contributions of two of Theodore von Kármán's former students, professors William R. Sears and Homer J. Stewart. Both men generously provided insights about their teacher which I could not have discovered elsewhere. Dr. William Pickering, a colleague during GALCIT and JPL days, and Shirley Thomas, an early biographer of Kármán, also shared their recollections with me. Dr. H. Guyford Stever, Kármán's assistant during the research phases of *Toward New Horizons* and the Woods Hole Summer Studies, was most helpful in this, as in other projects. I must also add a special thanks to Stanley Brozek, the present owner of 1501 South Marengo Avenue, Pasadena, California. He graciously opened his door to a stranger in December 1989 and told me the history of the home in the days during and after the Kármáns occupied it.

A number of archivists guided me through the research thickets. At the California Institute of Technology, the site of the Theodore von Kármán Manuscript Collection, Dr. Judith Goodstein and assistants Paula Agranat-Hurwitz, Shelley Erwin, and Bonnie Ludt answered many questions and provided assistance in the selection of photographs. The microfiche version of these papers, held at the Silver Hill, Maryland, branch of the National Air and Space Museum, was made available to me by Susan Ewing. The Chief of Special Collections of the United States Air Force Academy, Duane Reed, kindly took it upon himself to microfilm all the Theodore von Kármán manuscripts in his possession. He also supplied some very fine photographs, for which I am equally grateful. My friend and former coworker, William Heimdahl, Chief of the Reference Branch of the Office of Air Force History, allowed unusually liberal access to documents relating to Kármán's Air Force period.

Likewise, Jet Propulsion Laboratory archivist Julie Reiz went far beyond the ordinary to search her files for Kármán-related materials. Janice Goldblum, Assistant Archivist of the National Academy of Sciences, also dug deep into her collections to find materials on the Woods Hole Summer Study, as well as some Kármán photographs. Lieutenant Colonel Bill Reynolds, then on the U.S. Air Force Scientific Advisory Board secretariat, helped greatly by opening the board's office files and providing some vital leads. Saundra Taylor of Indiana University's Lilly Library acted with the speed of sound in providing a copy of an obscure but invaluable taped interview between Kármán and Shirley Thomas.

Finally, I must acknowledge personal debts. The late Eckford Sakaguchi, the truest of friends, was a constant source of sympathy and wisdom. As always, Alan Goldberg offered wonderfully practical advice. Roger White maintained a keen interest. Two cherished colleagues—William T. Y'Blood and George M. Watson—consistently cheered me on. My supervisor at the Air Force Systems Command, Colonel Oak De

Berg, listened long enough for me to answer my own questions. Professor John A. Schutz, my doctoral adviser at the University of Southern California, and Robert F. Phillips, my mentor in Air Force history, steadied me in moments of anxiety. Distinguished historians of long experience, they not only helped me to resolve technical problems in the manuscript, but over the years have taught me much about life. I must also thank Sheree Watt, owner of Casmar Enterprises, the talented person who turned page after page of handwritten, broken text into clean narrative pages.

My family rendered invaluable support throughout this project, and none more than my parents-in-law, William and Sarah Fetherson. Their concern and goodwill in this and all things has been constant and bountiful. Equally, my brother and sister, Elliott and Cheryl Gorn; cousin, Edward Gorn; and late uncle, Victor Klein, all maintained a stream of encouragement. Anne Gorn, my mother, did more to further this book than she may realize. Last, but really first, is my wife, Annette Gorn, who never doubted I would see this project through. Her quiet confidence assured its completion.

# The Universal Man

CHAPTER 1

# His Father's Son

Early one evening in 1936, a Cal Tech graduate student stood at the foot of a long driveway, working up the nerve to walk the wide black arc leading to his professor's doorstep. His mind wavered between excitement and anxiety. To his eye, the rambling Spanish villa on South Marengo Avenue in Pasadena, California, looked like many in the neighborhood. But his other senses disagreed. The address exuded an odd energy: gypsy violins animated the garden; a breeze carried the heavy scents of garlic and paprika; corks popped; and gusts of laughter escaped to the street. As he trudged mechanically up the path and onto the porch, the young man suspected that inside lay a thrilling, and at the same time intimidating, new world.

The moment the thick door crept back, he knew he had guessed right. Fumbling to pry it open, a man emerged from the din wielding an expensive cigar in one hand and a tall glass of (straight) Jack Daniel's whiskey in the other.

Middle-aged, a little below medium height and a little above average weight, he wore a formal dark coat and necktie. He had strong features; a prominent nose, clear grey eyes, and a bolt of wavy black and grey hair imparted a look of liveliness and vitality. His shuffling gait somewhat undercut the appearance of vigor. But his voice was his most unusual characteristic. He spoke his own English—low, slow, and heavy with the accents of his native Budapest—which left the uninitiated baffled. But what listeners failed to detect in language they discerned from observation: hands slicing the air for emphasis, a half-smiling expression, a shy manner, and a habit of concentrating full mental powers on the conversation. He commanded attention.

For an instant, the professor focused on the student standing in the doorway. Then, flashing a broad smile, he grasped his guest with an enveloping arm and led him into an expansive living room, stuffed like the rest of the house with Oriental furnishings. The young man soon found himself balancing a heaping plate of highly seasoned food and a tumbler of strong drink. Both proved less formidable than the crowd of people packed in around him. They came from all corners of the world and filled every foot of the living room, the big dining room, and the square kitchen. Some spilled into the garden. Actresses, Roman Catholic priests, spiritualists, physicists, artists, and military men mingled in tight proximity. The mixture of languages, nationalities, and occupations clearly delighted the host. Full of humor and bawdy stories, he swept back and forth across the rooms, igniting discussions on art, politics, and philosophy. Despite the crush and confusion, not a single attractive woman escaped his attention.

The mother of this unusual man presided over matters. A tiny figure seated in the sitting room on a throne-sized chair, she amazed and entertained her son's friends with her unfailing recall of their personal histories and preferences. His sister acted as hostess, ever watchful for empty glasses and urging the Hungarian cook to keep the platters flowing from the kitchen. Pleasantly intoxicated by the time things quieted down around 2 A.M., the young novice had experienced the first of many of these "very friendly, very jolly" affairs.[1]

The gatherings at the home of Professor Theodore von Kármán, witnessed by hundreds of students over the decades, tell much about him. They reveal a scientist with an extraordinary capacity for friendship and a man of unusual vitality. These qualities, so apparent at his parties, not only defined the Kármán persona, but explain much of his remarkable professional achievements. His scientific reputation rested on a series of profound insights on the nature of aerodynamics, which he demonstrated through a highly intuitive style of applied mathematics. In his long life he published more than two hundred scholarly papers, which collectively laid much of the technical basis of flight. Ultimately, he won international recognition as perhaps the foremost exponent of the discipline. Yet, because of the affection and respect he engendered among his colleagues, Kármán forged scientific cooperation and founded a number of powerful aerospace institutions. His likable personality led to close associations with leaders of government and industry no less eager than he to solve the practical problems of aeronautics. Finally, Kármán exerted a strong influence over American aviation through his students, three generations of whom benefited as much from his warmth and enthusiasm as from his mastery of the subject.

This unusual amalgam of scientific genius and personal magnetism stemmed from parental influence and the context of his childhood. Kármán grew up in Budapest, Hungary, in a middle-class Jewish family. His mother, Helen Kohn, descended from scientists, scholars, and men of practical affairs. The first of the line—Yehuda Loew Ben Bezalel, a famous sixteenth-century rabbi and mathematician at the Imperial Czechoslovak Court—invented an ingenious mechanical robot called the "Golem" of Prague. Ben Bezalel also befriended the renowned Danish astronomer Tycho Brahe, whose accurate observations of the heavens culminated in the planetary motion theories of his student, Johannes Kepler. Another prominent person in Helen Kohn's family was her grandfather, the author Moses Ben Menachem Mendel Kunitz. Kunitz wrote an important book of commentaries on the *Sefer ha-zohar*, the thirteenth-century Hebrew "Book of Splendors," which speculated on the nature of creation, the problem of evil, and the significance of good deeds. Finally, her father enjoyed considerable success as a tenant farmer near Budapest, raising cattle and bees and growing tobacco and wheat. His wealth afforded Helen the advantages of an English governess.[2]

Kármán's father, Maurice, known in Hungarian as Kármán Mor, had a less distinguished background. He, too, numbered learned men in his family, but none like those of his wife. His father owned a tailor shop in the provincial city of Szeged and made clothing for the local nobility. Maurice von Kármán achieved eminence not through family position, but by drive and brains. Born in 1843, he at first considered studying for the rabbinate, but chose philosophy instead, taking an undergraduate degree at the University of Vienna and a doctorate from the Pazmany Peter University of Budapest.

The Kármáns worked hard to make a stable home and had a devoted marriage. They occupied large apartments in the Jozsefvaros district of Buda and with each additional child added more living space. The quarters grew to seven adjoining flats, a long string of bedrooms, nurseries, and classrooms. The eldest offspring, Elemer, born in 1874, was followed a year later by Feri. Miklos, the youngest son, entered the household ten years later and a daughter, Josephine, came last. Between these two pairs of children the Kármáns lost one son, and to celebrate the healthy birth of a third boy on May 11, 1881, named him Todor, or "gift of God." His full name in Hungarian—von Sköllöskislaki Kármán Todor—became known in English as Theodore von Kármán.[3]

Clearly, Maurice von Kármán exercised the dominant influence in the family, a paterfamilias who directed the lives of his wife and children. He was remarkable in many ways. Bearded, slight, and ascetic in appearance, he projected at once benevolence and sternness. At home, he embodied patience and kindness, but in his career he could be quarrelsome, misanthropic, and uncompromising. Kármán succeeded in his profession in spite of these qualities. At the age of only 26, the young professor, who already had a fine scholarly reputation, received an invitation from the Hungarian minister of education to draft a blueprint for a modern, secondary school system. Kármán studied the French and German gymnasiums and proposed a plan of compulsory high school instruction controlled not by ecclesiastical but by state authorities. Three years later Maurice became Secretary General of the Austro-Hungarian Ministry of Education and put his reforms into effect. These measures brought competence and a sense of purpose to the system and many of his pedagogic methods gained widespread acceptance outside Hungary. He also experimented with secondary education by introducing a model ("Minta") gymnasium in Budapest, at which he tested teaching and curricular theories. His success in these endeavors resulted in a court appointment to supervise the education of the Archduke Albrecht, a cousin of Emperor Francis Joseph I. Finally, in 1907, the emperor granted him a hereditary title of nobility for his services. The ennoblement left little room for arrogance. Based on Kármán's only property, a small vineyard, the family was henceforth styled "little grapes."[4]

During the almost forty years between undertaking the educational reforms and receiving his title, Maurice von Kármán led a full life. Highly regarded as a philosophy and education professor at the University of Budapest, he taught courses, expanded his educational theories, and won a loyal body of academic disciples. His five offspring attracted just as much of his attention. In fact, his influence at home was nothing short of profound. For Todor, the deepest experiences of childhood centered on his father. He admitted in old age that Maurice von Kármán "dominated my life for as long as I can remember." He loved his mother but revered, and perhaps feared, his powerful father. The reverence was based on the benign side of this figure. The elder Kármán not only wrote his children's primers and fairy tales (which he later published), but oversaw their upbringing down to the slightest detail. He sought openly to influence their values and goals. Skeptical of the efficacy of public kindergarten and grammar school, he hired a former student to tutor them at home. He also insisted that each child not only study, but teach; hence, Todor learned from Feri, and taught Miklos. Young Kármán also participated in several required pastimes: fencing, hiking, skating, music, and trips to the countryside to visit his maternal grandfather. But mainly, the family looked inward to its cozy apartments, where great crowds of relatives gathered for parties and Maurice entertained eminent Hungarian intellectuals, artists, and politicians. The Kármáns enjoyed a rewarding life inside the compound.[5]

Yet, this happy existence had a dark aspect. Todor's kindly mother shouldered the frequent burden of soothing Maurice's fiery temper. His anger usually manifested itself in the workplace, but was inevitably felt at home. The situation deeply distressed Todor, in part because of his father's otherwise gentle nature. Convinced of his own rectitude, Maurice became embroiled in bitter fights with associates and superiors. Whether due to idealism, stubbornness, or a desire to right injustice, the behavior sent shivers down the young household. In one instance he wrote a vitriolic article against a colleague who had criticized the views of a mutual friend. Another time he unmasked a plagiarist with such vehemence that the denunciation discredited Kármán himself. Maurice von Kármán suffered for his intemperance with delayed promotions and withheld honors. Todor suffered, too. He wanted desperately to emulate his father, but these outbursts thwarted his efforts. Unable to be like him, he instead sought parental approval, going to great lengths to achieve it.[6]

At a young age, Todor underwent an experience that clarified the filial relationship. The event came about through childish innocence. When he was six, the boy's elder brothers noticed a peculiar talent. As Elemer and Feri sat one day waggling their pencils and counting multiplication tables on their fingers, Todor walked over to look at their work. He suddenly began reciting the answers to the problems. To their amazement, every figure proved correct. Even more astounding, in the coming weeks, they discovered he could multiply five- and six-digit numbers in his head, yielding sums in the millions. Their mother eventually became aware of this gift and asked how he did it. Todor could not say (and remained just as puzzled about it in later life). Nonetheless, she sensed her husband's disapproving reaction and managed to dampen her son's enthusiasm for a little while.

Inevitably, the secret got out. At one of the family parties, Todor stood by himself watching the relatives drink and enjoy themselves. Suddenly, on cue, Elemer and Feri took him by the hand and led him to the center of the room. Then one uncle, in collusion with the older boys, called for silence. He began to ask Todor multiplication problems of increasing difficulty. All eyes widened as the child's answers matched exactly the hand calculations that followed. The boy enjoyed the attention and, like an entertainer, knew instinctively how to please his audience. He paused expectantly before giving his answer and responded well to the applause and laughter that followed. But among the faces he saw his father's, which looked not the least pleased. It bore a stern and dark expression.[7]

After the guests left, Todor was ushered into the study for a talk. His father, whom he considered "a very wise man," asked him to do an extraordinary thing: banish mathematics from his mind for the next few years. The boy could hardly believe it. His father had always helped him do his sums and encouraged his work. Why should he be prevented from studying a subject for which he had such obvious aptitude? Maurice based his decision on traditional pedagogy. He had known boys of similar talent who squandered their abilities on mathematical tricks rather than serious study. To save Todor from this fate, he made him concentrate on a wide, liberal curriculum. He banned all math (but one algebra text) from the home and presented his son with books on geography, history, and literature. Significantly, the boy meekly accepted the harsh decree. Even though he disliked these subjects, for three years he carefully avoided mathematics in order to please his father. In fact, he obeyed Maurice's dictum to such an extent that he lost the knack of rapid mental multiplication and became a *slow* multiplier. Moreover, although Todor eventually spoke six languages, he could perform such calculations solely in Hungarian. Thus, he not only repressed this unique mathematical capacity; he reverted to the level of competence that existed *prior* to the incident with his father. Here it remained for the rest of his life.

As an adult, Theodore von Kármán frequently expressed gratitude to his father for nurturing "a general humanistic interest." He discounted as "exaggerated" the gift he once had, claiming it was unrelated to real mathematical ability. But young Kármán gained the broadening education at a heavy price: subjugating his will to that of his father and altering the course of his innate talents. Both had lasting effects on his life as a scientist.[8]

Psychically, Todor may have had a difficult time. But intellectually, Maurice equipped him marvelously well. He taught that science offered only one way of seeing the world. A sunrise might be viewed as God's will; as the basis of artistic expression; *or* as the fulfillment of Kepler's laws of planetary motion. Scientific knowledge, said the elder Kármán, merely organized sensory experiences in logical patterns, while art and religion interpreted the same phenomena emotionally. Thus, all three—religious, poetic, and scientific ways of knowing—had equal validity and significance to mankind.

From this principle Todor grasped the idea of a fundamental harmony in the world, not understood by purely rational or purely instinctive means. In this framework, God and science coexisted peacefully. Maurice von Kármán also imparted a breadth of thought which transcended not only epistemological categories, but narrow, parochial interests. He emphasized that discoveries should be shared and disseminated freely, not safeguarded like personal possessions. Nothing less than the "expansion of man's intellectual heritage" was the objective passed from father to son.[9]

The elder Kármán inculcated Todor not just with the importance of the basic laws of nature and the value of open discussion. He also believed that productive inquiry began with a mind receptive to new ideas. The fostering of intellectual curiosity affected the young Kármán more than any other of his father's precepts. Maurice piqued his interest in the physical world by posing simple questions: Why are the planets fixed in their orbits? Why are some raindrops large and some small? What are the principles of telegraphy? Observation alone would not suffice; the boy had to *understand* how these worked and the father went to great lengths to teach with examples and experiments.[10] Indeed, when Todor left home for his first day of school, he could not have been more thoroughly prepared to meet paternal expectations.

The Budapest that Theodore von Kármán entered in 1890 teemed with activity and optimism. The establishment of the dual monarchy of Austria and Hungary in 1867 finally ended almost 350 years of rule by occupation. The troubles began in 1526, when the Turkish armies inflicted a crushing defeat on the Hungarian forces at Móhacs. Sultanic hegemony gave way in 1686 to Austrian domination, following victories by Prince Eugene of Savoy, who captured Buda, western, and central Hungary from the Turks. The Hapsburgs established themselves officially in 1699 and for 150 years ran Hungarian affairs with a rigor sometimes rivaling the Ottoman Period.

Finally, in spring 1848, a coterie of prominent reformers led by Ferenc Déak, Jozsef Eötvös, and Lajos Kossuth, declared a free Hungarian government and raised an army to defend it. Hapsburg troops invaded and, with the crucial help of Tsarist forces, broke the resistance. Like the other European revolutions of the same year, it ended in abject defeat and harsh reprisals.

But the absolutists in Vienna finally agreed to make peace with Hungarian nationalism. After the loss of Italy in 1859, Emperor Francis Joseph I decided to work toward accommodation with Budapest. Negotiations dragged on until 1866, when the Austrians, defeated by Prussian forces, agreed to a compromise. The dual monarchy—which granted Hungary autonomy within its own borders and a large voice in imperial defense and foreign policy—went into effect in July 1867.

For those like Theodore von Kármán who came of age in the years after the agreement, it opened a world of possibilities. Nationalists and Monarchists may have fought bitterly in parliament, but essential political stability prevailed. Moreover, much economic and social reform took place. In the decades between 1867 and 1914, public debt fell and a dependable Austrian market brought good times to Hungarian agriculture, the main source of jobs and wealth. After 1890, national policies encouraged industrialization, which grew rapidly as a percentage of the economy. The population of Budapest and the other main cities experienced huge increases and public works proceeded apace. Finally, the vitality of the nation benefited from a series of popular reforms: modernization of the judicial system, greater balance (in favor of the government) in church-state relations, emancipation of Hungarian Jews, and, of course, educational restructuring.[11]

Kármán the school boy profited from all these changes, which liberated the national energies. Opportunities inherent in the new Hungary affected him from the day he left the family compound. He enrolled at age 9 in his father's open educational laboratory, known as the Minta Gymnasium, a "nursery for the elite." Its graduates included such renowned scientists as Edward Teller, Leo Szilard, George de Hevesi, George Polya, and John von Neumann. Under the direction of University of Budapest scholars, the Minta method stressed experiential learning: Latin from reading public statues, and advanced math (which

Kármán now studied voraciously) from statistical analysis. Memorization was forbidden and rules were arrived at by the students' own inductive logic. Maurice von Kármán also defied tradition by assigning graduate students to classroom teaching and prompting free discussion among students and instructors.

The younger Kármán succeeded brilliantly at the Minta, passing through the lower grades with ease. Maurice supervised his studies and continued to wield a powerful influence over him. In class, Todor came under the spell of the French mathematician and philosopher Henri Poincaré, who observed that science merely classified and arranged experiences. It could not provide final truths, because it treated only *particular* dimensions of thought. Indeed, scientific "facts" varied with time and new discoveries. He thus came to accept the possibility of events and knowledge outside the scope of regular human cognition. He believed physical laws had great value, but rested ultimately on resolution of the *discernible* contradictions in nature.[12]

Kármán's high school career ended with great promise. Along with a number of superior students, he entered a national competition for the Eötvös prize, awarded annually to the most deserving science or math student in Hungary. A nationwide committee screened all applicants and a select few were chosen to apply their imaginations to some highly complex mathematical problems. In 1897, young Kármán won the contest. But his family did not celebrate for long. Just as Todor turned his sights toward college and a career, his father suffered a mental collapse. The event occurred in public, at a banquet honoring the senior Kármán for twenty-five years of service to Hungarian education. After the presentation of poems and a festschrift volume, onlookers noticed strain and incoherence in his acceptance speech. Years of feuding with colleagues and rivals had weakened him, resulting in crippling migraine headaches. After the celebration, Maurice entered a Budapest sanitarium, suffering a nervous breakdown. Here he remained, isolated from his wife and children, for four years.

This episode devastated the Kármáns. Brothers Elemer and Feri took jobs to support the family. The prodigy also made sacrifices. Rather than enter a great foreign university, he stayed in Budapest to save money and assist his parents. Todor was deeply distressed by his father's illness. Maurice had been his closest companion, his mentor, and the center of his life. Nonetheless, Kármán enrolled at the Royal Joseph University of

Polytechnics and Economics, a former trade academy that had become a technical school through royal patronage. He pursued engineering rather than science or math because Maurice had persuaded him it was "nearer to everyday life" than the theoretical subjects. With his father in such frail condition, he did not dare challenge the sick man's wishes.[13]

Kármán did his best to content himself with the Royal Joseph. But many of the courses on hydraulics, electricity, and structures "were taught like baking or carpentry, with little regard for the understanding of nature's laws." He did make progress in other fields. He profited from courses in descriptive geometry, which trained his mind to visualize in three dimensions and liberated his imagination. He was introduced to French and German at the university and attained fluency in both. He achieved fair proficiency in English.

More important than any particular courses, university life afforded Kármán the opportunity to learn his own mind. In this case, the need to establish independence was especially acute. Until now, Maurice had all but overwhelmed him. But with his father ill and unable to advise, the freshman could begin to find his own way. He had always tried to please Maurice, but realized as an undergraduate the intellectual and emotional differences that separated them. First, he lacked the older man's passion for social causes and abstract justice. Second, while he lost the capacity to perform arithmetical tricks, Todor retained a brilliant memory and discovered he could learn varied subjects with ease. He also found his thought processes slow but deep, rendering it difficult to create on demand. Finally, lacking the suave ways of his brother Elemer, Kármán learned to charm through self-deprecating jokes and stories.[14]

Recognizing these qualities in himself, the student pressed on with his studies. He apprenticed himself to Donat Banki, a distinguished professor of engineering and hydraulics. Banki did not rank among the great scientists of the day, but he did have a knack for solving and explaining practical mechanical problems. In his lectures, he described complicated processes using simplified physical "pictures" of the underlying phenomena. This pragmatic methodology reminded Kármán of his father, and for good reason. Banki and Maurice von Kármán had been close friends for years, neighbors in Buda, and familiar figures in each other's homes. The student learned from Banki to avoid empirical rules in engineering and to concentrate on the cause of events.

Under Banki's direction, Kármán applied this lesson to a persistent problem in engineering, the clatter of engine valves. As the young

Hungarian later confessed, he bore the problem "like a woman carrying a child," laboring over it for some time. Suddenly, the answer came in a flash of insight; the noise must occur when resonances caused by valve motion operated in dissonance with the movement of engine pistons. Kármán then solved the puzzle mathematically, experiencing the exhilaration of correctly predicting the mechanical modifications necessary to stop the oscillations. He presented his findings to Banki, who accepted them for publication. It proved to the student what he had suspected for some time: his natural vocation lay in fundamental theory, in manipulating mathematics to better understand nature.

Despite Maurice's release from the sanitarium in 1901 and the resumption of close ties between father and son, by now the younger Kármán had discovered his own identity and began to orient his career according to his own tastes. The following year, at age 22, he graduated with distinction from the Royal Joseph with a Bachelor of Science degree in mechanical engineering. His thesis, published as "The Motion of a Heavy Rod Supported on Its Rounded End by a Horizontal Plane," revealed unusual insight for an undergraduate paper. A pedestrian subject, it still demonstrated good mathematical analysis and surprising content. True to Kármán's puckish humor, it described in mathematical terms the motion of a weighted sphere whose attached rod assumed a perpendicular position after being tipped to an incline; that is, a child's toy.[15]

While his father's influence slackened, Theodore von Kármán's education still set him on a course toward engineering, rather than a pure science. Before going ahead, he served a year of compulsory military service in the Austro-Hungarian artillery, which he accepted with little enthusiasm. When he left the army with a reserve commission in 1903, Banki suggested he return to the Royal Joseph and serve as an assistant professor of hydraulics.[16] Todor accepted and enjoyed the position. But he wanted more challenges and needed more money. Banki helped him again. He asked Kármán to be his partner in a consulting arrangement with Ganz and Company, one of Europe's leading manufacturers of locomotive engines. Although Hungary had just begun to industrialize, Ganz not only pioneered the three-phase motor, but sold the design to the Italian railway system, one of the most progressive in Europe. For three years, the two men collaborated on many important projects based on engineering research. Kármán gained valuable experience and discovered the essential nature of engineering from Banki, "a great inventor," who designed the first water-injection engine-cooling system. At Ganz,

Kármán learned a "feeling for practical engineering problems [which] profoundly influenced his later life."[17]

Useful as these experiences had been in providing the engineer's perspective, Kármán still craved the basic underpinnings of the phenomena he observed. Banki improved engine design by the selective application of theory to specific problems; his student sought to understand the fundamental principles of combustion and fluid motion first, *then* apply the research to machines and structures. Kármán called this the viewpoint of the learned man—'savant' in French, 'gelehrter' in German. He drew a distinction between "one who knows" and one who "makes science." Unlike Banki, who looked upon science as a tool of engineering, Kármán regarded it as an art, a means of arriving at the laws underlying the forces of nature.

The first of his papers to receive international recognition revealed just such profundity. Work at the Ganz machine shops led him to the subject, entitled "The Theory of Buckling and Compression Tests on Slender Columns." It had important implications for the structural elements of machinery, bridges, buildings, and aircraft. Kármán studied the point at which top-weighted columns buckled under heavy loads, hoping to provide engineers with a reliable theory to apply to all inelastic materials under similar pressure. The answer dawned on him suddenly, after days of relentless thought. Through a series of complicated mathematical calculations he arrived at a solution, and in 1906 the preliminary findings were published in the Hungarian periodical *The Magazine of the Society of Architects and Engineers.*[18]

These observations, which had important implications for research in applied mechanics, brought Kármán face-to-face with a personal dilemma: either continue his association with Ganz and Banki and enjoy a life of comfort in Budapest; or venture forth to develop his theoretical ideas. Maurice von Kármán exercised a decisive influence one last time. Broken by mental illness and deep professional disappointments, he felt unappreciated in his own country. He therefore urged his son to make a reputation abroad and use his latest research as a vehicle to advancement. The elder Kármán still exerted much influence, and Todor agreed to apply to the Hungarian Academy of Sciences for a fellowship to pursue the buckling problem. He decided to study in Germany, where immense strides were being made in theoretical physics and mathematics. Göttingen University in particular offered graduate work in mechanics under the eminent professor Ludwig Prandtl, perhaps the world's leading authority on the subject. Also on the staff were the great mathematicians Felix Klein and David Hilbert. The academy accepted Kármán's proposal and agreed to support him for two years at Göttingen. He left Budapest a local engineer of unusual promise; he returned to Hungary an internationally known scientist of the first rank.[19]

CHAPTER 2

# Scientist and Soldier

Theodore von Kármán loved Budapest, but thought of Göttingen with awe and delight. Chartered in 1211 and located sixty miles south of Hannover in the rich Leine River valley, the charming town had winding streets and fine structures. It had grown within a ring of fourteenth-century fortifications, behind which stood rows of half-timbered medieval houses on tree-lined cobbled lanes. Its wider avenues ascended toward a cluster of tall brick Gothic church towers. A fine city hall rose during Göttingen's prosperous days in the Hanseatic league, but during the Protestant Reformation, the area experienced hard times. Religious wars swept the region during the sixteenth and seventeenth centuries and only when King George II of England, acting in his capacity as Elector of Hannover, founded the university in 1737 did the town recover. It quickly became one of Europe's great centers of learning.

A lovely campus of venerable buildings—including a fourteenth-century Dominican friary housing a fine library—Göttingen University at first drew inspiration from its poets. In the nineteenth century such eminent Americans as Edward Everett, George Bancroft, and Henry Wadsworth Longfellow studied there. Brothers Jakob and Wilhelm Grimm, both faculty members, conceived their famous children's tales in the Göttingen libraries. But its greatness really ripened in the decades just before Theodore von Kármán's enrollment. While courses were offered in the liberal arts, medicine, and agriculture, its reputation rested on mathematics and science.

Perhaps the leading founder of the "Göttingen School" was mathematician Felix Klein. Thirty-seven years of age when he arrived at the university in 1886, Klein found profound mathematical connections among seemingly unrelated phenomena. He discovered unifying themes among all mathematical fields, which had particularly important implications for geometry, mechanics, and differential equations. Klein made significant contributions not only to pure but also to applied mathematics. Despite his own extraordinary theoretical work, Klein rejected the prevailing supremacy of abstract science and took every opportunity to nominate to university chairs men steeped in either applied mechanics or applied mathematics. He had two main objectives: to make Göttingen an even greater institution, and to put it at the disposal of the German nation. To do so, Klein forged alliances between pure and applied mathematics on one hand, and between industrial firms and the university on the other.[1]

Kármán's professors were crucial instruments of Klein's grand plan. One was David Hilbert, among the great mathematical thinkers of his generation. In 1895, Hilbert traded the robes of his alma mater, the University of Königsberg, for those of the Göttingen Mathematical Institute. Here he attracted students from throughout the world, including Americans Richard Courant and J. Robert Oppenheimer. Kármán and the others learned from him new techniques of applying mathematics to physics. Through integral equations, Hilbert elucidated important aspects of kinetic gas and radiation theory. He likewise contributed to quantum and relativity research and discovered axioms crucial to Euclidian geometry. Finally, in 1900, Hilbert published twenty-three questions, the answers to which laid the foundation for much of twentieth-century higher mathematics. Perhaps most important, he denied the validity of absolute mathematical truth, a view in tune with Kármán's own.

Felix Klein may have bestowed on Göttingen the institutional advantages of state-sponsored science and the practical value of applied mathematics; David Hilbert may have endowed it with a reputation for greatness in pure mathematics. But Theodore von Kármán left Budapest to study with only one man, the reigning genius of fluid mechanics, Professor Ludwig Prandtl. Unlike Klein and Hilbert, senior to him by thirty-three and nineteen years, respectively, Kármán was not much younger than Prandtl and settled in Göttingen only two years after him. Almost from the start, a thinly concealed rivalry developed between the thirty-one-year-old mentor and the twenty-five-year-old pupil. Despite the German's brilliant achievements, Kármán found it difficult to acknowledge his superiority, and a clash of wills ensued. The Hungarian's joie de vivre contrasted sharply with the shy, formal, pedantic habits of Prandtl.[2]

Kármán and Göttingen got along with not much more success. Though the city charmed him at first, its middle-class respectability left him cold. He lived well enough, renting a room near the university in a quaint old house. The life here and at a nearby beer parlor called the Black Bear Inn offered some of the social atmosphere he had imbibed in Budapest. But the pleasures of Kármán's private world could not offset the discomfort of adjusting to German academic practices. His first meeting with Prandtl foretold what lay ahead. The stolid professor offhandedly presented him with a "menu card" listing about fifteen subjects from which the protégé must choose his thesis. Dismayed but undeterred, Kármán rejected all proffered subjects and asked to be directed in further study of his main undergraduate interest—the buckling of inelastic columns. Prandtl showed little regard for this problem. His indifference, combined with the rigid caste system existing between professors and students, severely dampened Kármán's intellectual ardor. Over the months, the entire climate of the place became stifling. He regarded the popular dueling and drinking societies as caricatures of "Prussian stamina," from which Jews and Catholics were excluded anyway. The "austerity and formality" and inhospitality of Göttingen became too much. Despairing a life so alien to worldly Budapest and fearing his scientific project might be thwarted, Kármán resigned from the university in summer 1907 and enrolled at Charlottenberg Technical College near Berlin. But in the end Charlottenberg proved even worse, and in the fall he returned, chastened, to Göttingen.

The second start proved more effective. By luck the German armament manufacturer Krupp, seeking ways to prevent structural collapses at construction sites, presented Prandtl with a large hydraulic press to test columnar strength under pressure. Equipment in hand, Kármán could now undertake crucial buckling experiments, from which he quickly amassed the mathematical and empirical data needed for his dissertation. Completed in 1908, the results confirmed him as one of the preeminent authorities in applied mechanics. It was published the following year as the Kármán-Engesser double modulus theory of column behavior during load. His work explained mathematically the reaction of fibers in straight cylinders to the stress of heavy weight, which had wide-ranging implications for large structures borne by long, vertical supports.

By the time Kármán received the doctorate, he was eager to break with Prandtl. He disliked his coldness and found incredible his ignorance of women and of social graces. In a one-to-one tutorial setting, Prandtl had few equals, but in contrast to the witty and spontaneous David Hilbert, he was a dull lecturer. Nevertheless, Kármán had to admit Prandtl's genius. He sharpened the Hungarian's predisposition toward both theory *and* application. He made him realize the importance "of abstracting the basic physical elements in a complex process . . . and analyzing it with simplified methods of mathematics." While Kármán felt Hilbert the better mathematician, he admitted the tireless Prandtl should have won the Nobel Prize for his discovery of some of the fundamental laws of fluid motion.[3]

Only after travel abroad did Kármán realize the full import of Prandtl's theories. The young Ph.D.'s stipend ran out early in 1908, so he decided to abandon Göttingen. Father Maurice, still an influence, had always impressed on him the excellence of French scientists and philosophers. Thus, accompanied by Julius Veszi, a fellow son of Budapest whom he befriended at Göttingen, Kármán boarded a train for Paris. He embarked with Veszi not only because they shared the same homeland; his companion had three attractive daughters, one of whom was studying sculpture and working for a newspaper in the French capital. Kármán rented a room on the Left Bank, close by Marie Curie's lectures at the Sorbonne and other seminars at the University of Paris. In the meantime, he delighted in Parisian café society and sampled the city's many nightspots. For two splendid weeks Kármán basked in the pleasures denied him at Göttingen. Then, on the morning of March 21, 1908, after an all-night party near the Sorbonne had run its course, he stopped at a favorite coffee house on the Boulevard St. Michel to warm himself and pass the time before returning home. Chance events at the dawn of this day changed Kármán's life.

As he sat musing about Göttingen and his career, Veszi's eldest daughter Margrit appeared before him. She had ventured out to do a newspaper story on the Englishman Henry Farman's aeronautical exploits in a Voisin biplane, saw Kármán in the window as she passed on the street, and came in to enlist his aid. Farman's recordbreaking attempt to sustain the first two-kilometer flight in Europe would occur that day at 5 A.M. at Issy-les-Moulineux, a small army parade ground southwest of the city, on the Left Bank. The flight of the Wright brothers on December 17, 1903, still shrouded in secrecy due to patent litigation, added anticipation to the event. So did the 50,000-franc purse awaiting Farman. Miss Veszi prevailed upon Kármán to drive her to the airfield. At first he declined, tired from a long night and not especially interested in a flying "box kite made of sticks, wood, and paper." But out of regard for her father, and not a little interest in her, Kármán agreed and they got into his car and raced to the airfield.[4]

They arrived just before five and found a small, odd assortment of literati and street urchins watching in the twilight as the Voisin was pushed out of a hangar at the south end of the field. Farman then threaded himself through the tangle of wire braces onto a seat on the lower wing. The engine turned over with a bang and as the propeller started to turn, Kármán watched expectantly as the pilot wheeled the clattering machine 150 feet down the field. When the aircraft reached a distance of 500 yards from a marker on the far side of the parade ground, the Englishman gave the beast full throttle and up it went, making lazy circles from the starting line to the turning point and back again. At the end of the second pass, he maneuvered the fragile steering rudders so that the plane sailed safely between two poles planted at the finish line. Farman had traveled 2,005 meters in 3½ minutes, setting a world record for an officially witnessed flight. The crowd was awestruck by the event.

Three things about the display excited Kármán's scientific imagination: How had the Voisin been able to overcome Sir Isaac Newton's theory of air resistance and particles, which seemed to pose an insurmountable barrier to flight? How had the aircraft's wings supplied enough lift to overcome the plane's considerable drag? Finally, how had the fifty-horsepower Renault engine produced enough power to levitate its own weight, as well as that of the airframe and Farman himself? Kármán began to investigate. Initially, he looked upon this miraculous event from an engineering viewpoint. He had learned much about modern engine technology from Donat Banki, and pondered the solution in terms of lightweight power plants. It was said the Wright brothers had built a 200-pound engine. Charles Manly, an assistant of flight pioneer Samuel P. Langley, developed the world's first radial propulsion system, which weighed just 125 pounds. Kármán held informal discussions with several French airplane manufacturers about designs for lighter and more powerful engines. But these talks led to nothing practical and weeks of inactivity left Kármán discouraged and indecisive—should he return to Hungary or seek work elsewhere? The burden was shortly relieved in a note from Prandtl, asking him to take a laboratory assistantship in Göttingen's new airship wind tunnel, being built under contract for the

Zeppelin Company. Since the proposal would allow him to pursue his budding interest in aeronautics, he overlooked its source and accepted.[5]

Kármán returned to Göttingen in the fall of 1908. Suddenly, the theories of Prandtl assumed far more importance to him than in the days of buckling columns. He reacquainted himself with a paper given by his mentor four years earlier at the Third International Congress of Mathematicians. Here Prandtl suggested a profound discovery on the motion of fluids around stationary objects: "boundary layers" of viscosity existed along the borders of such solid forms, interacting with adjacent free-moving fluids. The minute friction that developed along the surfaces of such shapes, he found, could have a profound influence on overall flow pattern, thus retarding efficiency of motion. Based on a brilliant intuitive insight, borne out both by approximate mathematical calculation and water canal experimentation, Prandtl described a phenomenon of nature that had eluded the mathematical as well as the experimental factions of fluid mechanics. His theory incorporated the techniques of both schools, and Kármán recognized its genius. Furthermore, two years later, Prandtl made a historic scientific leap by deducing that the same boundary layer that existed in fluids must also act on the air. In other words, he introduced the world to the idea of "drag" in aeronautical design.[6]

Kármán came back to Göttingen just as his teacher was realizing the fruits of these exciting discoveries. Prandtl had won not only the Zeppelin contract, but became an active participant in the design of new aircraft and oversaw construction of the first German wind tunnel. Kármán made his initial foray into aeronautical publications with a paper on engines, a subject much on his mind since the encounter with Farman. The article, written for the *Journal of the Society of Hungarian Engineers and Architects,* sought to acquaint his countrymen with his recent experience at Issy, with the Parisian power plants, and with the inevitable economic importance of aviation. Perhaps Kármán saw an opportunity to encourage the further growth of industrial firms springing up around Budapest. At any rate, the paper cited "recent . . . undisputed successes" in airplane flight tests during 1908. Kármán called attention to two successful French engines: one an improved automotive design, and the other made expressly for aircraft. Modified from auto- and boat-racing purposes, the Antoinette, which was similar to Farman's Renault, weighed about 286 pounds and delivered one hundred horsepower from sixteen cylinders. The Levavasseur Co., builder of the Antoinette, reduced weight by eliminating the flywheel, adding cylinders, and placing them in a V-shape to cut bulk at the crankcase and crankshaft. But Kármán's enthusiasm was reserved for a truly ingenious aviation propulsion system, the R.E.P. (after its inventor, Robert Esnault Pelterie). The R.E.P. design arranged its cylinders radially, and yielded sixty horsepower from a 216-pound engine. Although Kármán faulted several of its innovative structures, he still suggested that such power plants offered significant opportunities for heavier-than-air flying.[7]

While this article showed Kármán's ripening interest in aviation and sounded a clarion call to Hungarian engine builders to examine the French designs, it lacked any sign of interest in applying his mind to the science of flight. This awakening came slowly, after a time of readjustment to Göttingen and immersion in Prandtl's new endeavors. He did not like the city any better than before, but determined to make the best of the situation. For the next three years he resided in a comfortable house just a few minutes from the campus. He and four other boarders became good friends. They nailed up a sign outside the residence with the exotic inscription "El Bokarebo," a composite of the lodgers' first and last names (the "bo" of which stood for Max Born, later winner of the Nobel Prize for quantum physics). When Kármán learned of a nurse wishing to retire to the country and care for a few mentally ill patients, he persuaded her to come to the university and instead be their housekeeper! He also continued to frequent the Black Bear Inn, where after nights of drink and song he and his mates roamed the streets and switched shopkeepers' signs, just to aggravate the sturdy citizenry. Many important university figures peopled the Black Bear tavern, not least of whom was Ludwig Prandtl, sometimes observed stirring his coffee and peering down into his cup to observe the eddies of motion across the inky fluid.

These deeds and pastimes added enjoyment to an otherwise difficult period. Prandtl's offer to Kármán came with the title Privat dozent, the purgatory of German academic life. Professors normally headed their own institutes; associate professors acted as paid faculty and researchers. Privat dozents, however, were temporary workers awaiting permanent appointment elsewhere, with no tenure, no faculty voting rights, and no salary except for whatever the students agreed to pay. Until an associate vacancy opened, men like Kármán could do nothing but wait. As a friend observed, the best way to hasten promotion would be to sink the ship that recently carried Göttingen's mathematicians to a conference in New York. Kármán suggested a more devious, if less deadly, plan. A privat dozent, he joked, had the *right* to teach, and the *duty* to marry the daughter of his superior. In the meantime, Prandtl kept the Hungarian busy with the dirigible project. Count Ferdinand von Zeppelin conceived the idea of a rigid, nonmotorized airship at the turn of the century. The German army expressed interest, and Felix Klein persuaded the government to underwrite Prandtl's investigations of its flight characteristics. Kármán not only collaborated in building the airship wind tunnel, but undertook some of Göttingen's first aeronautics experiments and taught courses in mechanics.[8]

Between 1909 and 1911 his involvement with the wind tunnel and the mysteries of fluid motion led him "away from other fields of mechanics and focused [him] on the young science of flight."[9] Twenty-eight years old when he fully committed himself to the study of aerodynamics, he hardly embarked on it as a youthful whim. Nonetheless, Kármán became involved in a discipline still in its infancy. The Wright brothers' unprecedented technical achievement occurred just as the scientific underpinnings of aeronautics were coming to light. In 1897 Frederick W. Lancaster, a brilliant English engineer and inventor, applied mathematical rigor to the work of countryman Sir George Cayley. Cayley argued in the 1840s that Sir Isaac Newton's theory of high air resistance from atmospheric molecules could be overcome by harnessing an engine to an aerodynamically shaped structure. At the end of the century, Lancaster demonstrated this primitive theory of lift mathematically. Ludwig Prandtl then explained much of the force opposing motion with his conception of the boundary layer. Both discoveries influenced profoundly the course of aircraft design and propulsion.[10]

Prandtl's boundary layer theory had broad applications not only to aircraft, but to airship and nautical vessels as well. To better understand its characteristics, he asked a doctoral student named Hiemenz to study the turbulence caused by water moving past a solid cylinder. He would then observe the point at which the eddies separated themselves from the viscous boundary layer surrounding the tube.

But when Hiemenz lowered a rod into a channel and set the fluid in motion, he discovered persistent, violent oscillations at some rates of flow. This phenomenon frustrated his research on the boundary layer mechanisms. Prandtl dismissed it as an anomaly, an experimental deviation: Hiemenz was first told to grind the cylinder to painstaking tolerances. When this failed to cure the maelstrom, his professor directed him to improve the symmetry of the channel.

Kármán happened on the problem quite accidently. He and Hiemenz shared a laboratory, and as the stray eddies defied one mechanical solution after another, Kármán asked Prandtl's miserable assistant the same question morning after morning: "Herr Hiemenz, is the flow steady now?" Each time he answered unhappily, "It always oscillates."[11] Despite the press of work in the dirigible project, the turbulence problem lingered in Kármán's mind.

One Friday, he decided to invest a weekend and try to clear up the mystery. He began with a hunch: the solution was mathematical, not mechanical. Wake was occurring due to some basic law of nature. He made two assumptions. First, the roiling water represented vortices pouring downstream from the cylinder in two parallel trails, both shed at almost the same instant. This motion implied instability since minute differences in the timing of the birth of these rotating bodies would eventually destroy the smooth flow pattern. His second assumption was based on the well-known fact that fluid motion behind symmetrical objects yielded *alternating*, not synchronized, vortices; that is, the eddies did not roll off both sides of the tube simultaneously, but first off one edge, then the other. After working out some general mathematical approximations, Kármán showed his intuition to be correct.

> As I examined this motion, the whole solution suddenly leaped into my mind and I saw clearly that this configuration becomes stable when there is a definite geometric arrangement of the vortices. This arrangement occurs only at a certain relationship of two distances—the distance between two single consecutive vortices and the distance between the two rows of vortices. Or to put it another way, instead of marching two by two, the vortices are staggered like lampposts along both ends of a street.[12]

The following Monday, Kármán could hardly contain his excitement as he revealed his findings to Prandtl. Its originality was transparent. "You have something," his mentor said in his usual understated way. "Write it up and I will present your paper."[13] Late in 1911 Prandtl read the report to the Göttingen Scientific Society under the title "On the Mechanism of the Resistance That a Moving Body Experiences in a Fluid." Although based on a series of simplified calculations, it caused a sensation among fluid mechanics and aerodynamics researchers. Kármán followed the paper with a second, more complete one, arriving at the same conclusions through more exacting computations. In it, he appended experimental test data from Hiemenz's tank and the Göttingen wind tunnel which bore out the behavior of the vortex pattern suggested in the mathematics.

The results of his first foray into aerodynamics brought Theodore von Kármán international recognition and eminence. But more important, his methods represented the first time he incorporated fully the intellectual totems of his teens and twenties: his father, Donat Banki, Felix Klein, David Hilbert, and Ludwig Prandtl. His own inclinations were equally important. From the age of thirty until the end of his life, Kármán's work would be typified by this highly personal approach to problem solving. His ideas began with intuitive inspiration, took form in mathematical calculation, underwent testing in the laboratory, and were finally applied to real engineering problems.

Many practical applications resulted from the Kármán Vortex Trails or Streets, names quickly identified with the discovery. Rotating eddies became associated with such occurrences as "singing" wires on biplanes and the turning propellers on naval ships. Stationary structures such as bridges, radio towers, and powerlines also experienced vortex instability during blustery conditions. All such objects were gradually redesigned to reduce dangerous oscillations and buffeting. Aircraft, dirigibles, and ships, in particular, underwent significant external modifications to inhibit drag induced by the Kármán Streets. For instance, by forming an airship hull so that the turbulent trails *followed* the downstream contours of the vessel (rather than separating from the solid body almost on contact, as in the case of a cylinder), the cigar-shaped vehicle would move through the air with fifty times the efficiency of a disk the same diameter. Hence, the well-known term, *streamlining:* an object designed so its vortices flowed as far down its own stream line as possible. Retractable landing gears, slender airfoil profiles, and smooth fillets joining upper wings to fuselages all contributed to the "clean" lines of modern aircraft. They embodied a revolution in the contours of objects traveling through air and water.[14]

Crucial as the Vortex Trail may have been in establishing Kármán's scientific stature, neither it nor the airship studies conducted for Prandtl occupied all his time. In fact, between late 1908 and early 1912, much of his work had nothing to do with fluid motion or aeronautical design. With his roommate, physicist Max Born, he tackled a problem posed by David Hilbert: whether solid matter did or did not consist of atoms in constant motion. Physicists had tried to solve the problem through temperature measurement, implying greater atomic activity at higher heat. Kármán and Born devised a three-dimensional mathematical model of vibrating atoms fixed in a regular pattern. This lattice formation, though scoffed at at first, came to be accepted as a true picture of crystalline atomic structure, useful in predicting the behavior of materials at low temperatures. Nor did Kármán abandon his dissertation subject. He did further studies on the buckling resistance of columns, deformation of thin-walled tubes, and the strength of corrugated cylinders. Indeed, Kármán's scholarly output began to reach its stride. At the rate of one article or presentation every 4.5 months, he established an enviable publications record and maintained the pace for the rest of his life.[15]

But despite the young scientist's favorable attributes—hard work, scientific distinction, and an engaging personality—he now approached his fourth year as privat dozent. Thirty-one years of age, Kármán had no permanent position and no sign from the Ministry of Education of being in line for one. Despairing his own prospects, he applied for and won a professorship in applied mechanics at the College of Mining Engineering located in Selmeczhanya, Hungary, a school founded in the eighteenth century by Empress Maria Theresa. But he was soon disappointed. He ended up teaching the theory of machines. He had no interest in gold mining, the academy's raison d'être, and found the students indifferent and the equipment poor.

Kármán arrived there in fall 1912, but within weeks decided to pack his bags and return once again to Göttingen, leaving the job temporarily in the hands of a friend. On his arrival, Felix Klein summoned him to his office. Why, Klein asked, had he accepted a position at such an academic backwater? The Hungarian explained his frustrations simply: he had become tired of life as a junior researcher. Klein now "guaranteed" him the next worthwhile chair that became vacant. Unfortunately, this post, at the University of Munich, had already been promised to the son-in-law of a retiring faculty member. Kármán contented himself with the second best opportunity, to be professor of aeronautics and mechanics at the Technical University at Aachen, Germany. Any disappointment vanished when Klein also obtained for Kármán the directorship of the Aachen Aerodynamics Institute, a weighty title for someone so young. Significantly, Ludwig Prandtl played no apparent role in finding an appropriate position for his star pupil.[16]

Young he may have been, but Theodore von Kármán knew his own mind. He liked everything about Aachen. Centered in the prosperous Rhineland at the corner of the Belgium, Dutch, and German borders, and only a short train ride from France, the town had the bustle and cosmopolitan flair he missed in Göttingen. After more than six years among stolid Protestant burghers, Kármán relished the worldly, leisurely atmosphere of Aachen, former seat of medieval emperors and bastion of Roman Catholic influence.

Built on the site of the Roman spa Aquisgranum, Aachen straddled western and middle Europe. From this unusual position, Kármán could look, as it were, out facing windows: one toward French and maritime civilizations, the other beholding German culture. Historically, the city was neither German nor French, but polyglot. Referred to as Aix-la-Chapelle in France, it had been both home and burial ground of Charlemagne, whose cathedral, begun in 796, still dominated the city. Charlemagne made the place his northern capital and a seat of western learning. From 936 until the sixteenth century, most German kings received their coronation from its throne. France conquered Aachen in 1794, and retained it until 1815 when it was ceded to Prussia. Thus, diverse and colorful, the city offered a joy of living familiar to a son of Budapest.[17]

Kármán arrived at his new home on a midwinter day in February 1913. His initial reception at the Technical University was not much warmer. An institution of one thousand students devoted to mining and metallurgy, its faculty reacted with puzzlement to the new man with boyish looks and a determination to make Aachen famous for aeronautical science. His singlemindedness stemmed partly from his relations with Prandtl. Clearly, a degree of professional respect had developed between the two men. But the senior professor's attitude, captured in the remark that Kármán had the knack of "skimming off the cream" while others labored on the milk, did little to soften personal differences. Kármán carried with him feelings of "friendly [but intense] rivalry" for the Göttingen Aeronautics Institute and for Prandtl in particular.[18] The urge to compete would take some years to satisfy.

The first challenge occurred during the early period of Kármán's career in Aachen. Prandtl and his staff sought a mathematical theory to account for induced drag: that is, the resistance that developed as a countervailing force to aerodynamic lift. The Göttingen institute found that induced drag originated in forces acting on aircraft wings. Vortices at the leading edge of a wing moving through the air raced over the top surfaces faster than the bottom, resulting in a pressure differential and lift. But vortices of equal strength developed at the wings' trailing edges, causing proportionate drag. Prandtl and his colleagues discovered that long, slender wing shapes distributed lifting properties across the full wing expanse, giving a greater advantage to the leading than to the trailing vortices, and yielding more lift than drag.[19]

Göttingen gained a second advantage over Aachen when Prandtl took the lead in organizing aviation science. The opening in 1912 of the national German Research Establishment for Aeronautics resulted largely from his urgings to the Interior Ministry. Using the Göttingen institute as a model, the government in Berlin established projects, personnel, buildings, test equipment, and a budget for the new institution. Prandtl thus scored on two fronts: by discovering new, fundamental laws of aerodynamics; and by shaping the creation of a powerful aeronautical organization. Yet, the clear disparity between Göttingen and Aachen did not deter Kármán. He sought nothing less than the transformation of the Aachen institute into a "world recognized research establishment." The best—and really, the only—weapons at his command were his own mind and energy. Aachen would call forth from him a peculiar complex of abilities: "vision in planning, intuitive genius in research, [and] inspired teaching."[20]

During his first weeks and months at the university, Kármán gauged academic life at his favorite institution, the local café. He found a fine one near the town spa, and often stayed late into the night smoking cigars, drinking coffee, playing chess, and jotting ideas on tablecloths. Another of the scientist's early mainstays was Hugo Junkers, professor of engines at the Technical University, inventor, and industrialist. This famous figure had worked for years to adapt thermodynamics to practical aeronautical engineering. Until Kármán's arrival, Junkers was the only Aachen instructor capable of teaching aviation science. Gradually, profits from patents on such inventions as the free piston engine and the portable gas water heater freed him from teaching. He advised the school to establish a chair in aeronautics, but since only twelve students were registered in the subject, his successor, Professor Hans J. Reissner, lectured on mechanics as well. As the first institute director, Reissner also undertook construction of the original Aachen wind tunnel and demonstrated aptitude in propeller design. But his real interest lay in aircraft structures and after a few months he left for a position at the University of Berlin.

Fortunately, when Kármán took the reins of the aeronautics department, Junkers still lived locally and the two men established a close partnership. To prosper, the institute required such a connection. The Technical University survived on the financial support of Rhineland iron and steel firms, as well as grants from the Luxembourg government. Junkers connected the institute to the financial resources of German aircraft industries. He gave Kármán practical yet innovative technical ideas that attracted lucrative commercial contracts. Junkers pressed his friend to experiment with thick, fuel-bearing wings, internal bracing and cantilever structures, and sleek, strutless, all-metal designs.

The young director first undertook improvements on the institute's physical plant. He redesigned the existing wind tunnel, located on the roof of the laboratory. Its trumpet-shaped open end was closed and converted to the more efficient continuous circulating system favored by Göttingen. By early 1914, he had renovated the facility and could take on Junker's projects. Kármán then began hiring a staff. He started with mathematician Erich Trefftz, the nephew of Professor Carl Runge of Göttingen. Shortly afterward, Kármán and his associate devised a theory of airfoil design which could be applied to any number of aeronautical shapes. The Kármán-Trefftz profiles resulted in wings with a radical new feature: trailing edges with finite angles sandwiched between the upper and lower airfoil surfaces. The principle of the movable trailing edge, as plotted on Aachen blackboards and tested in its wind tunnel, contributed to the Junkers J-1 transport aircraft. Introduced in 1915, it featured a cantilevered all-metal structure and became a model of its kind.[21]

This initial breakthrough illustrated Kármán's peculiar talent for scientific application, "an instinct for seeing which problems were likely to be important from the engineering point of view, which had intrinsic intellectual interest and which of his [colleagues] were likely to make a success of them."[22] But he had far less talent as a man of action. In exchange for basic lessons in flight dynamics, several German air force pilots agreed to teach him to fly. His Rumpler Taube aircraft, a reliable trainer, had the unfortunate tendency of tipping forward as it landed. During one of the lessons with a military copilot, Kármán landed his plane nose-first into a potato field. Staggering to the nearest road to get help, he was promptly fined twenty marks by a passing policeman for the crime of illegal trespass. This episode ended the Hungarian's career in the cockpit.[23]

But his life with military air forces did not end on a bed of tubers. When Austria declared war on Serbia on July 28, 1914, Kármán still held a commission in the Austro-Hungarian army, being obliged to take reserve training every other year. In fall 1914, the service recalled him to active duty as 1st Lt. Theodore von Kármán, and he found himself on a train rolling eastward across Germany to Budapest. This call to arms for World War I postponed for almost five years the progress he had hoped to achieve at the institute. His own aerodynamics research was also stymied from 1914 to 1918. Yet Kármán's wartime experience added a vital dimension to his professional and personal maturation. He would eventually control a large budget, oversee many important engineering problems, grasp the importance of international scientific cooperation, and learn the "art of 'getting along' with generals and admirals."[24]

Unfortunately, such rewards did not greet him at the railway station in the Hungarian capital. As in all armies, the man and his talents were soon parted. Kármán reported to the same unit he had served with since 1903, the heavy battery unit of the 61st artillery regiment. But a congenital hearing loss in his left ear, for which Kármán wore an amplifier all of his adult life, resulted in a transfer to Montur Depot on Coepel Island, near Budapest. Here he "created some disorder in the distribution of uniforms" but enjoyed the pleasure of being near his parents, whose other sons had received assignments abroad. However, in February 1915 his scientific knowledge at last became known to the Hungarian commanders, who directed him to design the city's large gun emplacements to repel advancing Russian forces. Kármán had already undertaken related work in inventing a crude slide rule that told artillerymen the distance and position of enemy tanks.

Not until August 1915, almost a year after he reported for active duty, did Kármán's aeronautical knowledge become realized and harnessed. So far, Austria's ally Germany had only dispatched dirigibles for night attacks on France and the United Kingdom, but in summer 1915 Berlin decided to employ aircraft as offensive weapons. To contribute to the new strategy, Kármán was reassigned to the Austro-Hungarian Aviation Corps and made director of research. At the Military Aircraft

Factory at Fischamend, near Vienna, he began a lifelong affiliation with military aviation. The air corps may have been pitifully weak in flying machines and equipment, but it lavished facilities and staff on the young scientist. With as many as forty assistants, he transformed a Zeppelin hangar into an experimental station, complete with a wind tunnel for propeller experiments.

Here he and his associates dissected German and Italian planes to learn their secrets; perfected (through mathematical calculation) Anthony Fokker's synchronization of machine gun and propeller; and invented a fuel-tank sealing device that prevented explosions triggered by the penetration of bullets. These developments helped prepare the airplane for its attack mission. The Fischamend group also produced a prototype of a vertical flight reconnaissance machine, conceived as the replacement for the cumbersome, combustible airship. This primitive helicopter, designed by Kármán and tethered to the ground by cables, rose on two counter-rotating propellers powered by three 120-horsepower engines. The Aachen director was summoned to Berlin late in 1917 to advise the German high command on the efficacy of helicopters to supply the capital in case the Allies laid siege. He reported persistent stability problems that hindered the effective employment of the new weapon. Under orders, he continued to study possible technical solutions. Months of fruitless work ensued. Finally, in August 1918, by which time the fate of Germany had become clear, Kármán received a pass to return home.[25]

The next months brought upheaval for him, his family, and his country. The first disaster struck some years before. Maurice von Kármán had collapsed and died in 1915, after delivering a lecture. The younger Kármán, desolated by this "first really deep blow" in his life, raced home to comfort his mother. Luckily, the demands of Fischamend absorbed his energies and prevented prolonged grieving for the person who had done most to shape his personal and scientific outlook. Nonetheless, he felt a keen sense of loss for many years. Helen von Kármán carried an even lonelier burden. Not only had Theodore been assigned to Vienna, but another son had marched off to the Balkan campaigns while a third boy and her only daughter were garrisoned in the Rattaro Fortress, Dalmatia.

Three years later, after failing to perfect his helicopter, the scientist again found himself en route to Budapest to relieve his mother's loneliness. Once there, he beheld a city in ferment, restless with the imminent defeat of Germany and the dual monarchy. The Austrian emperor Charles, who succeeded Francis Joseph, abdicated the throne in November 1918. Led by Count Michael Károlyi, a democrat and pacifist, the Hungarian parliament declared the country a free republic on November 16, just five days after hostilities ended on the Western Front. Despite early progress in dividing large estates among the peasants, Károlyi resigned in March 1919 when the Allied powers assigned Transylvania to Romania, rather than cede it to Hungary. A Socialist regime gave way quickly to the Communist rule of Béla Kun, comrade of Nikolai Lenin.

Since the new regime condemned militarism, Kármán saw no good reason to stay in uniform. He mustered out immediately and collected his back pay. But his return to science and Aachen would not be so easy. Allied regulations forbade travel by enemy officers until the signing of a peace treaty. During the political turmoil in Budapest, he was invited by one of his father's former students to help the Ministry of Education put Hungarian higher education on a modern footing. Kármán accepted and joined the progressive Károlyi government, hoping to fulfill his late father's dream of universities equally devoted to research and teaching.

When the cabinet resigned, friends urged him to stay on and serve Béla Kun as undersecretary of education for universities. He agreed reluctantly, and during summer 1919 made wide curricular changes in the natural sciences and medicine, for the first time introducing atomic physics, modern biology, and psychoanalysis into Hungarian classrooms. Kármán's political career ended in August 1919 when the Communist administration fell to invading Romanian armies, bent on revenge for Hungarian efforts to reclaim Transylvania. Béla Kun fled to Russia and Kármán, fearing for his own safety in the ensuing ransack of Budapest, hid in the home of a friend. Meantime, he cabled the Technical University in Aachen, found his old position still open, and quickly laid plans to escape Hungary for Germany. But the tumultuous year in Budapest taught him two important things. First, he must pursue his own gift for science, not emulate his father's passion for educational reform. Second, the experience "saved me for all my life from having any belief in Communism—I saw it in operation and that was sufficient."[26]

Surviving war, revolution, and his father's untimely death, the thirty-eight-year-old Kármán ended this hard chapter of his life on the rails from Budapest to Aachen. As the conductor called out Bratislava,

Vienna, the Carpathian towns, and, finally, German cities, he felt a sense of homecoming, rather than leavetaking. He relished the thought of resuming real scientific inquiry and took comfort in the wartime survival of all the family but Maurice. Kármán arrived in Aachen in November 1919 and found the city miraculously untouched by battle, but the institute almost ruined with neglect. Closed for five years except to garrison soldiers, the aeronautics building needed a thorough reconstruction, cleaning, and painting. With typical improvisation, the director enlisted some occupying Belgian troops to rebuild and restore the laboratory in exchange for free lessons in aeronautics.

Using even greater persuasiveness, he convinced his mother and his sister Josephine (known to everyone as Pipö) to leave Hungary. Actually, they were moved by events. After the Allies forced the Romanians to withdraw, the monarchist party under Admiral Nikolaus Horthy agreed in June 1920 to the bitter Treaty of Trianon. It dictated catastrophic terms to the eastern half of the dual monarchy, ceding nearly three-quarters of Hungarian territory and two-thirds of its inhabitants to Yugoslavia, Romania, Czechoslovakia, and Austria. In light of the turmoil, Kármán worried about the safety of the two women. He also feared they would be lonely. Maurice had been dead five years and Theodore's brothers had their own wives and children. He proposed they join him in Germany and make a new start. After an emotional departure from friends and relations, in 1921 Pipö and Helen followed him to Aachen. Here the three Hungarian emigrés established themselves in the life of the university. Kármán, meanwhile, earned an international reputation not only for aerodynamics research, but for raising a second-rate academic institution to a position of worldwide prominence.[27]

CHAPTER 3

# From Aachen to Pasadena

After a brief period of homesickness, Kármán, his mother, and sister found a stable and happy existence in their new surroundings. They decided to rent a house across the border in Vaals, Holland, where property was cheaper and a modestly paid professor could conduct his affairs in stable Dutch guilders rather than mercurial German marks.

The household had all the comforts of the one in Budapest: a fine salon, three guest rooms, a library, and ample space for social events. Here Helen and Josephine made a home for him, and a routine ensued. During the week, Kármán commuted by trolley to Aachen, concentrating the first few months on reviving the moribund laboratory. Despite the workload, the director regularly invited his students to the house for informal "tea seminars," during which Theodore, Mrs. von Kármán, and Pipö served light refreshments as the young guests talked about the institute and their private lives. Such gatherings broke tradition in German pedagogy, where academic rank was observed strictly, even on social occasions. Most weekends saw an even more daring violation of custom. Colleagues, assistants, students, and visitors—greeted by meats and sauces, wines and whiskeys, pastries and coffee, laughter and ideas—wedged into the Kármán home for lively parties. Host, hostesses, and a Hungarian cook participated in these impromptu, free-form gatherings with as much zeal as their visitors.[1]

The atmosphere of contentment contributed to Kármán's scientific output. He had been diverted from aerodynamics research for almost six years, but lost no time committing long pent-up theories to paper. In 1921 he published three important articles, the most crucial of which, "On Laminar and Turbulent Friction," ramified Prandtl's theory of the boundary layer. Written in the Hungarian's fortieth year—which Prandtl acidly called Kármán's "age of discretion"—the new work "contributed to a much better understanding of the frictional resistance of fluids."[2]

He and his colleagues succeeded in reformulating the boundary layer equations so that comparisons between theory and experiments could be undertaken. First, he integrated Prandtl's work into a single momentum equation. Then, rather than rely on his mentor's partial differential equations, Kármán borrowed (from K. Polhausen) an integral relation in which a general solution resulted from assumptions on the distribution of velocity. It enabled Kármán to describe the boundary layer as a complete mechanism, using a method that came to be known as the Kármán-Polhausen approximation. This new application of a well-known mathematical technique had crucial practical implications, allowing an accurate prediction of drag on surfaces moving through air or fluid. It affected not only the design of aircraft and future rockets, but was of critical importance to petroleum- and hydraulics-related industries, which were deeply concerned with the frictional motion of liquids through pipes.[3]

On the strength of discoveries such as these, Kármán gradually transformed Aachen into an aeronautics powerhouse, the rival of Göttingen. Students the world over learned of the institute and its atmosphere of free inquiry and sought admission. Yet the director's success in this regard did not rest solely on scientific reputation. Kármán also established a cosmopolitan tone for the institution. Not only he, but his mother and sister also, spoke several languages fluently. He had at his command Hungarian, German, French, Italian, Yiddish, as well as "bad English," which he called the international scientific tongue. Kármán stirred foreign interest in Aachen as he lectured to audiences over the length of Europe, explaining with exuberance the unfolding of aeronautical knowledge.[4]

But innovative research and international appeal both took second place to the self-described basis of his success. "I have," he remarked, "some art in teaching, to explain complicated things rather simply."[5] Kármán attributed this affinity to a "direct inheritance" from his father, who delighted in nurturing young minds and in fostering the exchange of ideas. Maurice's son also loved to instruct, and based his classroom work on intellectual honesty. "I don't fool myself," he admitted. "I either understand or I don't understand."[6] This simple principle focused Kármán's mind on a clear, direct transmission of fundamental knowledge to his students. Complications could always be added as the pupils matured. Kármán's pedagogy entailed much more than mere communication of science.

In my teaching at Aachen I tended to be personal with, and to take a deep interest in, the development of each student with whom I came in contact. In class I often scanned the sea of brown, blue, and green eyes, seeking the occasional spark of understanding that flashed here and there. I made it a point to remember the student who had caught my eye, talk with him, and then eventually invite him to my house.[7]

The "personal" interest took many forms. Kármán often appeared unexpectedly at university beer halls, and his presence, which flattered the students, brought large numbers to his table to discuss aeronautics. In his rounds at the institute laboratories, he often chatted with pupils about the progress of their experiments. But, just as likely, he inquired about homesickness and wayward sweethearts. He also counseled the parents of particularly gifted children, suggesting suitable schools and preparations for higher education. He performed such a service for a wealthy Budapest banker whose son wished to study mathematics. Kármán's advice to him had merit. His offspring, Dr. John von Neumann, won an international reputation as father of the digital computer and co-inventor of the hydrogen bomb.

Naturally, the principal contact between Kármán and his pupils occurred during seminars and lectures. In these sessions he coaxed them to discuss openly whatever technical problems they uncovered. Usually, fellow students supplied the answers, which led to new discussions and more discoveries. He flavored his lectures with pictorial examples to prove theoretical points, likening a vortex to water and soap powder going down a bathtub drain. He described inertia as two monkeys hanging at either end of a rope, suspended from a pulley; one, through fast climbing, might overcome his own weight, as well as the "dead" pounds of his lazier partner. No wonder his students came to refer to themselves as the "Kármán circus."[8]

Thus, the Aachen Aerodynamics Institute achieved eminence after World War I due as much to Kármán's pedagogical talents as to his scientific achievements and cosmopolitan ways. Yet, there was a fourth ingredient in the recipe. Unlike Professor Prandtl, Kármán wanted to share theoretical discoveries not only among German academics, but in international forums as well. In the drive to add luster to the institute, the goal of global cooperation made sense. In practice, Kármán encountered the resistance of scientists with bitter wartime memories. Many asked why they should join hands with men whose countries had pursued the war with such bloodiness. Nonetheless, in 1921 Kármán and the mathematician Tullio Levi-Civita of the University of Rome gambled against failure and called the first International Congress on Aerodynamics and Hydrodynamics in Innsbruck, Austria. The idea sprang from Josephine von Kármán. If the Kármán household could host friendly gatherings of Frenchmen, Germans, Englishmen, and Italians, surely something could be done to reestablish ties between the world's applied mechanics community. Maurice von Kármán's internationalism fostered this outlook in Pipö and Theodore and, as foreigners in Vaals, the family could credibly adopt the broad perspective. Brother and sister paid the costs of organizing the conference themselves and issued invitations to representatives of the two former alliances: British, French, and Americans; Germans, Italians, Austrians, and Hungarians. Despite trepidation as the date in 1922 approached, the risk paid off. Informal and comradely, it "was an unusual success, and the brotherhood of science was never more apparent."[9]

Shrewdly, Kármán took the opportunity of the Congress to read an important paper. Entitled "On the Surface Friction of Fluids," it declared his interest in finding a general theory of turbulence. He reviewed the existing literature and concluded that to truly understand turbulent friction transfer and comprehend the empirical evidence, "the safeguiding hand of theory" needed to be marshaled. He predicted such an explanation would emerge from statistical calculations and from "a happy idea, which has not been found."[10] He often returned to this subject in future papers and conferences.

Two years after Innsbruck, the Kármáns and friends organized another Congress, meeting this time at the Technical University at Delft, Holland. Two hundred attended the First International Congress of Applied Mechanics, and steps were taken to formalize future meetings. Again taking the opportunity of an international audience to air some of his more daring ideas, Kármán delivered a paper that haltingly answered his own challenge issued in 1922. "On the Stability of Laminar Flow and the Theory of Turbulence" provided an initial sketch of a statistical explanation of chaotic motion. The Aachen director pondered the problem by comparing the rate of energy increase during major disturbances to the speed of dissipation resulting from friction and small oscillations.[11]

Thus, Theodore von Kármán looked upon international conferences as opportunities to further scientific cooperation. At the same time, these meetings afforded a rare platform for his best ideas and provided an unparalleled opportunity to further the reputation of Aachen. One final technique to build the institute involved industrial consultations. While the Ministry of Transportation in Berlin did supply some much needed funding, a large part of Kármán's operating budget derived from business sources. The wind tunnel and laboratories of Aachen were energized by tests and experiments conducted for private firms.

Hugo Junkers led all such benefactors. Just after his return to Aachen after the war, the Hungarian undertook significant consultative assignments for him. During a two-week working visit to the industrialist's villa, Kármán received fees worth half his annual salary. In this and other periods, Junkers probed the scientist's mind on many subjects. The aerodynamics of the thick (fuel-bearing) wing for long-distance aircraft continued to fascinate the German magnate, as it had before the war. Junkers also wanted Kármán to explain why he favored conventional aircraft, rather than seaplanes, for transatlantic travel. The answer was characteristically simple. Amphibious craft required costly calculations both on ship *and* plane aerodynamics. "The cheaper the design," said Kármán, "the better the result." In addition, the Aachen director helped his friend develop arguments that led to the award of a patent for Junkers's famed J-1 aircraft. At first, the patent office in Berlin refused to recognize the claim. But Kármán convinced a judge that the crux of Junkers's invention lay in the continuous self-supporting beam structure of the J-1's wings. No other manufacturer had designed an aircraft whose airfoils flexed independently of the fuselage and supported the weight of the engines on their own strength. The patent protected the design not just in Germany, but in many foreign countries, including the United States.

Junkers's gratitude greatly helped the Aachen institute. Kármán also enjoyed the patronage of the von Zeppelin Company, a connection begun in his postdoctoral days at Göttingen. In 1924 he visited their airship factory at Friedrichshafen, near the Swiss border. During World War I, some 120 rigid-keel Zeppelin dirigibles flew as terror weapons over England; now the company sought to fulfill an American contract for a transatlantic behemoth. Kármán was asked to redesign the classic dirigible profile to eliminate a recurring problem: in-flight elevation of the airship nose. Powerful turbulence often accompanied this phenomenon, threatening to tear the hull asunder. In a short length of time, the scientist uncovered the mystery. The culprit was not the common cigar shape, but an uneven flow of air over its skin. He provided Zeppelin with a workable theory of pressure distribution. The uneventful maiden flight of the *Los Angeles* from Lake Constance, Germany, to Lakehurst, New Jersey, bore out his calculations.[12]

By 1925, then, Theodore von Kármán had taken long strides to satisfy his objectives at the Aachen Aerodynamics Institute. His ongoing research on turbulence placed him in the front ranks of aerodynamics scholars. His teaching, atypically student-oriented for its day, attracted a following from Europe, the Americas, and Asia. His organization of international science spread his fame and carried his force of personality to colleagues the world over. His ties to Junkers and Zeppelin yielded substantial grants and lent an empirical, engineering character to the facilities. In five short years since returning to Aachen, Kármán had succeeded in rivaling Göttingen and Prandtl.[13] By mid-decade he had reached a professional juncture in which new opportunities would be received eagerly.

"What is the first boat you can take to come to Pasadena?" This simple sentence, imprinted on a telegram to Theodore von Kármán without explanation, would eventually transform his life. Although he could not foresee the implications of the cable at the time, the Aachen director already had in mind some fundamental change in his situation. Still in early middle age, full of practical and theoretical projects, and widely liked and respected by his international colleagues, he was bound to attract interest.

The country that eventually commanded his services badly needed an infusion of aeronautical science. During the first decade of the century, Wilbur and Orville Wright led the world in the pursuit of flight dynamics. But by the teens and twenties, American predominance gave way to European mastery, based on research in fluid mechanics. Despite rudimentary wind tunnel laboratories at Stanford University and the Massachusetts Institute of Technology (MIT), theoretical aerodynamics was slow to take root in the United States. Even the National Advisory Committee for Aeronautics (NACA), founded by Congress in 1915 to spur aeronautical knowledge, concentrated its laboratories on experimental, rather than mathematical, research. Purely advisory from its establishment until the Air Commerce Act of 1926, the NACA did succeed in enforcing some coherence among public and private aeronautics institutions. In the wake of the legislation, the study and application of aviation technology became more structured. Gradually, universities became centers for the theory of flight; NACA and the National Bureau of Standards contributed basic research; the aeronautical industry designed and developed aircraft; and the armed forces tested them for conformity to specifications.

Despite increasing clarity of functions, the theoretical aspects lagged. Through the first quarter of the century, those engineering schools that taught aeronautics paid little attention to science, emphasizing empirically demonstrated principles. In most such departments, aeronautics failed even to gain acceptance as a recognized discipline. Thus, regardless of the antipathy toward Germany in the period during and after World War I, those Americans interested in the fundamentals of flight had little choice but to study in the aerodynamics institutes of the former enemy. In articles written by U.S. scientists for the popular press, the fame of Göttingen and the other institutes spread to America. Such interchanges finally brought one of Ludwig Prandtl's students to the United States. Professor Max Munk worked from 1920 to 1926 as an aerodynamics consultant for the NACA Langley Aeronautical Laboratory, overseeing a vigorous program of experimental wind tunnel research. Munk, who essentially introduced America to aerodynamics, taught the NACA staff complex mathematical formulations to explain airship resistance, lift, and induced drag. Published Göttingen research on airfoil advances also found a receptive audience at NACA. Indeed, Joseph A. Ames, chairman of NACA's executive committee and professor of physics at the Johns Hopkins University, wrote repeatedly that aeronautics must be studied as a pure science, the fruits of which would result in greatly improved airships and aircraft. Ames attributed this insight to Ludwig Prandtl.[14]

Göttingen and Prandtl may have been celebrated in U.S. aviation circles; yet it was Theodore von Kármán who ultimately symbolized aerodynamics in America. The main reasons may be found in the mind of Robert Andrews Millikan. An eminent experimental physicist, Millikan, born in 1868, received a Ph.D. in physics from Columbia University in 1895. He taught for almost twenty-five years at the University of Chicago, pursuing three research interests: measurement of the electrical charge of electrons; substantiation of the photoelectric equation posited by Albert Einstein; and exploration of cosmic ray phenomena. Notable successes in these fields led him in 1921 to the California Institute of Technology (Cal Tech). Here he not only directed the Norman Bridge Physics Laboratory, but served as chairman of the Cal Tech Executive Council—in effect, as the university president.

Millikan achieved spectacular success in establishing Cal Tech as a world-renowned center of scientific learning. In his quest to make Cal Tech great, he was aided by several factors. Winning the Nobel Prize in Physics in 1923 for his electron experiments not only bolstered his own stature, but that of the institute as well. He attracted distinguished faculty from around the world, building on existing departmental strengths. Millikan possessed a keen sense of the scientific worth and personal qualities of those he appointed. Finally, he had the vision to imagine Southern California as the crossroads of the nation's science and technology establishment.

In his efforts to fulfill this promise, Robert Millikan enjoyed no greater success than in Cal Tech aeronautics research. The program actually started in 1917, four years before his arrival, when the campus was known as the Throop College of Technology. It began with an anonymous grant of approximately $5,000 and the hope of wartime subsidies from the federal government. New classes were announced with high enthusiasm. A wind tunnel, said the Throop catalog, "will immediately be built . . . and a graduate course will probably be provided." Indeed, a forty-mile-per-hour open return wind tunnel did rise on the Pasadena campus during the first year. In 1918 two men received faculty appointments: Albert N. Merrill, a veteran aviator who designed the tunnel and oversaw its construction, became a research assistant in charge of operations; and Dr. Harry Bateman, an eminent Cambridge University mathematician, assumed the position of professor of aeronautical research and mathematical physics. Despite brave attempts during these early years, no real department materialized nor were any aeronautical degrees granted. Merrill continued to undertake experiments in the tunnel and Bateman occasionally instructed postgraduate mathematicians and physics students on theoretical hydrodynamics and elasticity.[15]

During the early 1920s the situation began to improve. Robert Millikan's son Clark, a graduate of Yale University in physics, enrolled in several of Bateman's courses and developed a fascination for aeronautics. He earned a Ph.D. from Bateman in viscous flow theory, collaborated with Merrill on wind tunnel research, and learned to fly. Merrill entertained some inventive ideas on aircraft design (such as movable wings) and the younger Millikan assisted him in constructing a working model. For expertise on design detail and controls, they recruited Professor Arthur L. Klein, an experimental physicist who had recently received the doctoral degree from Cal Tech. Merrill's project—which did finally produce a flying aircraft—drew together Bateman, Merrill, Millikan, and Klein, a nascent Cal Tech aeronautics center.

Cognizant of this group's activities through Clark and his three associates, Robert Millikan sought ways to exploit its potential for the school, and for Southern California as a whole. The answer may have occurred to him in 1924 at Delft, Holland, at the First International Congress of Applied Mechanics. Here, conference organizer Theodore von Kármán and the Cal Tech chief had their initial meeting. Millikan recognized unusual "accomplishments and ability" in his younger colleague and must have admired Kármán's tantalizing paper on turbulence. The Hungarian's informal style likewise appealed to Millikan, typically American in appreciating the direct approach. Finally, he understood Kármán in the European context, having studied at Göttingen and the University of Berlin.[16]

After this brief encounter, the two men parted company. But in 1925 a rare opportunity to join forces presented itself. Daniel Guggenheim, scion of a powerful mining and smelting dynasty, decided in that year to designate a portion of his wealth to endow several major aeronautical schools. Guggenheim chose this particular cause as a result of his son Harry's service as a World War I naval aviator and liaison officer to U.S. aircraft industries. New York University (NYU), which had opened a small but coherent aeronautics program in the mechanical engineering department, would benefit first. The NYU grant had particular appeal since the philanthropist and his son lived in New York. Hence, on June 15, 1925, the elder Guggenheim announced his intention to donate $500,000 for three endowed aeronautics chairs, a laboratory building, a wind tunnel, a propeller laboratory, and salaries for assistants. But such largess was only a downpayment. By the end of 1925 word began to spread of plans to initiate a national program entitled the Daniel Guggenheim Fund for the Promotion of Aeronautics. Harry Guggenheim discussed it with President Calvin Coolidge and Commerce

Secretary Herbert Hoover late in December at the White House. He proposed to spend $2.5 million for the undertaking and assemble a board of eminent trustees to govern it. The president and Mr. Hoover gave their unqualified support.[17]

Robert Millikan learned of events in New York and Washington from an article in the Pasadena *Star-News*. It named NYU, MIT, and the University of Michigan as probable recipients of Guggenheim money. Not to be outdone, on the night before Christmas, 1925, Millikan wrote to Harry Guggenheim requesting half a million dollars for Cal Tech aeronautics operations.

Millikan then packed a bag and boarded a train for New York to make his arguments in person. On January 6, 1926, he urged Guggenheim father and son to include the West Coast in their aviation philanthropies. Why not build on Cal Tech's incipient aeronautics school with a laboratory, a new wind tunnel, and salaries for two research professors, a wind tunnel operator, a model maker, and four graduate students? In short, he asked for the wherewithal to launch a genuine aerodynamics institute in Pasadena. Millikan made a persuasive case. He described the possible contributions of two outstanding Cal Tech professors of mathematical physics, Paul Sophus Epstein and Richard Tolman. He also carried with him the support of Donald Douglas, a leading airplane manufacturer located in Santa Monica, California. Millikan related the obvious advantages of locating an aeronautical institution in a region of year-round good climate.

But he concluded his remarks with a warning to Daniel Guggenheim: he would be making "the greatest mistake of his life if he [did] not give a considerable part of the money . . . to Cal Tech."[18] His reason showed real vision. Millikan predicted that Southern California would soon become the nerve center of the nation's aviation industry, requiring an aerodynamics institute for scientific advice. Vast, inexpensive real estate for hangars and test facilities, in addition to favorable labor conditions, virtually assured the Los Angeles area a high proportion of aeronautical activity, provided it had technical backing. "All right," the senior Guggenheim said, "I'll give you the money, if you get me from Europe somebody [who] knows the fundamentals—the theoretical fundamentals—of aviation and would do this [at Cal Tech] . . . as Prandtl did in Germany."[19] Millikan listed several possible candidates, but only two men stood out: Prandtl and Kármán. The Guggenheims preferred Prandtl due to his age and reputation as "the father of all aeronautical sciences." The meeting ended with a verbal commitment to fund the Cal Tech project and Millikan was asked to look for a director.[20]

Actually, no real search would be made. Since the Cal Tech chairman had just won the main point—agreement on an aeronautics school for the Pasadena campus—he decided not to challenge the Guggenheims' choice of director just yet. Clearly, however, his first choice was not the Göttingen professor, but Theodore von Kármán, whom he knew and respected. Physics professor Paul Sophus Epstein, an old friend of Kármán, reinforced Millikan's sympathies. Born in Russia and educated at the universities of Moscow and Munich, Epstein had been recruited to Cal Tech in 1921 from Leiden University. He and Millikan both felt Kármán would bring to the institute vigor, youth, diplomacy, and a receptiveness to new ideas absent in the shy and pedantic Prandtl. The Aachen director had also proven himself able to build a first-class aerodynamics institute with minimal resources in a short period of time, perhaps a foretaste of success in Pasadena.

Ten days after Millikan's session with the Guggenheims, the fund for aeronautics was officially initiated. Less than two weeks later, Millikan wrote to Harry Guggenheim, gently suggesting that Aachen must be considered equally with Göttingen in the choice of a director. Anxious to sign and seal the papers for the Cal Tech aeronautics institute, Millikan traveled again to New York and on April 30, 1926, met with Harry Guggenheim to iron out details. He stayed on until early June to make a formal proposal to the fund's board. On June 7 Harry Guggenheim and his associates awarded Cal Tech $180,000 for a new laboratory building, a wind tunnel, and associated equipment; $100,000 for ten years of faculty and staff salaries; and $25,000 for five years of research-related costs.

Yet, the problem of leadership remained unsolved. To force a decision, Millikan took a double gamble. Before the Cal Tech board had formally approved the $305,000 grant, and even before telling Harry Guggenheim about his candidate for director, Millikan directed Epstein to write Kármán in Aachen and ask whether he would care to spend fall 1926 consulting in Pasadena. A $4,000 stipend was tendered. On July 7, the Cal Tech chief finally sent a letter to the younger Guggenheim, informing him of the pending offer. He suggested Geoffrey I. Taylor of the United Kingdom as a second choice, and Ludwig Prandtl (a "somewhat impractical personality . . . far less useful to us than v. Kármán") a distant third. Luckily, Guggenheim, who had considered bringing over Prandtl as recently as Millikan's last New York visit, acceded to the bold stroke, and the Cal Tech faction waited nervously for a reply to Epstein's proposal.[21]

After almost two anxious weeks without a response, Millikan followed Epstein's note with a cable. But the telegram reached Aachen before the letter and both had to be forwarded to Ostende, Belgium, where the Kármáns had gone on holiday. Unaware of these facts, Millikan assumed that Epstein's correspondence had already been received and approved. His telegram simply asked the earliest date on which the Hungarian could sail to the United States. Baffled, Kármán cabled Epstein for clarification. Nonetheless, just six days after receiving Millikan's mysterious message, he wired Pasadena and expressed an interest in visiting Cal Tech. Epstein's letter, which finally arrived four days later, was reassuring. It presented an expansive picture of a new, generously funded institute and a welcoming atmosphere for scholars from German universities. Moreover, the $4,000 stipend, more than many tenured Cal Tech professors earned in a year, would leave plenty in his pocket, even after deducting the costs of travel and expenses. Epstein proposed August 15 as a date to embark on his American debut.

Kármán may have said yes, but two hurdles remained, both of which postponed arrangements. First, his mother objected to such overseas sojourns, especially to a land she thought "ridden with gangsters." To placate her, Pipö agreed to go along, to take care of his domestic needs and augment his fractured English with her good command of the language. The second barrier to Millikan's proposition involved an offer from the Kawanishi Machinery Company of Kobe, Japan. Kawanishi's directors had asked Kármán to spend six months at their works, advising on construction of the country's first wind tunnel. He thought he could rid himself of the Asian junket (and his mother's even sharper objections) by asking for a fee of $4,500, double the original Japanese offer. To his amazement, they agreed. He thus took a leave of absence from Aachen for the 1926–27 semesters, planning to be in America from September to Christmas, and in the Orient during the first half of 1927.

Kármán wrote to Millikan on August 14 with the good news: "Spending some months in your circle is the most delightful thing I can imagine. I hope to be of assistance to you in this development of your institute for aerodynamics." Epstein received an equally cheerful note, stating "a visit in California, particularly in constant exchange with you and Mr. Millikan, seems to me very exciting." At this early date, the

Aachen director may not have persuaded himself of "any permanent change of continent." But he did respond to the Pasadena invitation with speed and enthusiasm, suggesting he at least had begun to entertain the idea of a life in the United States.[22]

Kármán always relished change and variety, and in 1926 and 1927 he experienced both in abundance. He and Pipö set sail aboard the S.S. *Mauritania* and anchored at the Port of New York on Friday, September 24, 1926. The Guggenheims had announced their arrival some weeks before, building anticipation in aviation circles. The pair were met at the pier by retired Rear Admiral Hutchinson Cone, Guggenheim fund vice-president, who conducted them to Hempstead House, the immense Guggenheim mansion at Port Washington, Long Island.

The next two days turned out to be "extraordinarily pleasant." Kármán marveled at the opulence of the first American home he ever visited. Built from remnants of several seventeenth-century French chateaux and constructed on a huge scale, it lent a serene background for discussions on U.S. aeronautical progress. During the talks, Kármán suggested, and his hosts approved in principle, a series of modern engineering handbooks. These were later published as *Aerodynamics,* by William Frederick Durand, the standard text. More important than this agreement, a lasting impression was formed that weekend. By Sunday afternoon, Harry Guggenheim realized Millikan had made a brilliant choice for Cal Tech. "Of all the good scholars" he had met, "only a few stand out, and those few . . . have wisdom as well as intellectual capacity. If it interested him, [Kármán] could make a great ambassador, or a great . . . anything. I think that is true of the few great men with whom I've come in contact. They are very few."[23] On the Monday, brother and sister boarded a train for Pasadena. During the following days they savored the excitement of the New World floating by their car. They reached the Pacific coast at the end of September, where the main work of the first American trip would unfold.

On the Cal Tech campus, Kármán quickly detected problems in the embryonic aeronautics program. First, he encountered a divided faculty. Harry Bateman, an able but shy mathematician, rarely spoke to Albert Merrill, an aviation inventor of strong mind. The perspectives of the theorist and the practical engineer represented two different approaches to aeronautics, and Kármán made a mental note to draw the two men, as well as the two disciplines, into closer cooperation. The second hurdle could be overcome more easily. Prior to Kármán's arrival on the quiet campus at the fringe of the Southern California suburbs, Clark Millikan and Arthur Klein had been hard at work on plans for a new wind tunnel, ten feet in diameter and capable of two-hundred-mile-per-hour air speeds. Theirs, like the old Cal Tech tunnel, featured an open-ended design popularized by the French engineer Alexander Eiffel and commonly used in the United Kingdom. The Hungarian visitor objected to this method. A closed, circulating system (like the ones at Aachen and Göttingen) would significantly lower operating costs by eliminating the influence of the outside atmosphere. After only six hours of consultation, Kármán had all but torn up the Millikan-Klein drawings. Moreover, he suggested placing the motor *inside* the tunnel, *within* in the airstream, as close as possible to the propeller. Klein resisted this idea strongly, raising questions about the accessibility of the engine to repair. But Kármán argued that his design would greatly reduce the frequency of breakdowns by eliminating a long driveshaft and many bearings. To settle the debate, he sketched the enclosed system on the back of an envelope and submitted it to Robert Millikan. Despite the advice of Klein and his own son, the Cal Tech leader sided with Kármán.

The decision did not just involve factors of operating efficiency and maintenance. A closed system also required far less space than its competitor. The final architectural plan took advantage of this factor, placing the tunnel at the core of the new building. The design left room for a surrounding ring of laboratories, offices, and classrooms, linked by narrow corridors and stairways. Klein did win one point over his new colleague. He wanted and got a fireman's pole for descents from the third floor, edging out Kármán, whose customary desire for comfort led him to recommend an elevator.

In fact, the pole better suited the freshly minted Guggenheim Aeronautical Laboratory at the California Institute of Technology (GALCIT). Casual, like the California culture itself, GALCIT became an intimate company of scholars, employing only five regular faculty members. It endured as a closely woven group. The GALCIT principals may have wavered on the wind tunnel, but by the time Kármán left the campus late in October, the new school's educational policies had not only been agreed upon, but published. A Cal Tech bulletin entitled "New Courses in Aeronautics" appeared during that month. It listed new offerings on the theory of aerodynamics, described classes on airframe and engine design, and announced research fellowships. Most important for the future, the bulletin unveiled a cooperative teaching venture in which practical instruction on aircraft structures would be taught by engineers of the Douglas Aircraft Company of Santa Monica. Students enrolled at GALCIT could now take four-year degrees in science or engineering with an aeronautics emphasis. After 1927, they could graduate with the Masters of Science in aeronautics. Despite its small size, untested curricula, and unfinished facilities, the laboratory aspired to greatness from the start, promising to "make a center of the first importance in Southern California for the development of both the theoretical and practical phases of aeronautics."[24]

Kármán felt nothing more could be accomplished at Cal Tech for the moment, so in late October he set off with Pipö for the East Coast. In Pasadena he had spoken to several large, enthusiastic audiences on aeronautical subjects. Under Guggenheim auspices he delivered similar lectures across the United States. Robert Millikan knew why the Hungarian did so well on the circuit, despite his mysterious accent and foreign manner. "He is a master of the subject," noted the physicist, "and wonderfully skillful in presenting lucidly a subject which really involves a lot of advanced mathematics."[25] Kármán's abundant charm and many anecdotes warmed audiences in all the Guggenheim-funded schools: the University of Michigan, NYU, and MIT. His travels revealed a high proportion of European aeronautics instructors at Michigan and NYU and relatively few Americans teaching applied mathematics. This situation perplexed Kármán, who took it upon himself to redress the imbalance in future years. Actually, the first opportunity came sooner than expected. On the Cambridge, Massachusetts, campus a student named Frank Wattendorf plucked up the nerve to introduce himself to Kármán after hearing his first lecture. Intrigued by his approach to basic aerodynamic theory, which was not well known in the United States at the time, Wattendorf applied to study with him at Aachen. He enrolled in 1927, becoming the first American at the institute, and stayed until 1930. During his three-year tenure, the young man rose in his professor's favor, becoming like "a member of [Kármán's] family [and his] closest associate."[26]

The eastward tour did not consist only of academic speeches. On the way, he and Pipö visited the Grand Canyon and marveled at its scale, indeed at the size of all the natural phenomena they encountered. Just as amazing in its own quiet way was Dayton, Ohio. Here he spent lunch and an afternoon with Orville Wright, "sincere and unassuming," yet far better versed in the fundamentals of aerodynamic theory than Kármán had imagined. Just as much at odds with the popular view of the Wrights as simple inventors, Kármán saw a wind tunnel in Orville's laboratory which dated from 1902. Wright explained with pride that during the year before Kitty Hawk he and his brother had logged hundreds of hours testing wing shapes on the small machine.

The American tour ended in Washington, D.C. Between the third and ninth of December, 1926, the Hungarian delivered a series of lectures on aeronautics at the Smithsonian Institution. The program was chaired by Edward P. Warner, assistant secretary of the Navy for aeronautics. Here Kármán spoke on propeller theory, boundary layer formation, induced airframe drag, and air resistance. He drew large crowds of academicians and aviation enthusiasts. On the ninth and tenth he delivered similar talks to a group of university presidents whose institutions benefited from Guggenheim funding. Finally, Kármán ended his first American sojourn with lectures before the leaders of the NACA and the U.S. Army Air Corps. As Christmas 1926 approached, he accompanied Pipö to New York where she boarded a liner to France and he embarked by train for San Francisco, en route to Japan. The American trip had been a huge success. Harry Guggenheim and Robert Millikan delighted in their "find" for U.S. aeronautics. Kármán had generated much enthusiasm (and much press) for aerodynamics on both coasts. He had made many new friends and associations. Most important, he found in Pasadena and GALCIT a relaxed and intimate environment, qualities that appealed to his taste for informality and close human contact.[27]

If America began to beckon in this period, Japan presented a pleasant interlude. Kármán no sooner arrived in the country than Kawanishi representatives brought him to a resort for a week of rest. In Kobe he finally met with the company directors, who asked him to design a wind tunnel to complement the firm's large aeronautical laboratory. He agreed to build one along the lines of the Aachen facility. But in working with the Japanese from the top levels of management to engineers on the shop floor, he found some inadequacies. Despite the Kawanishi eagerness to raise Japan to world eminence in aviation, lack of military-industrial coordination left private firms in sole command of the aeronautics infrastructure. The Imperial Navy was interested but not active in such efforts. Second, their engineering education rewarded fidelity to existing methods, rather than fostering an appreciation of the underlying scientific processes. In lecturing to the company's engineers, Kármán not only touched on the main technical points, but stressed the importance of obtaining a "feel" for the problem at hand by applying originality to even the simplest assignments. Finally, the Aachen director found impediments to scientific endeavor in the Japanese social order, which seemed to him intensely hierarchical and ritual-bound. But as he later admitted, many of these negative influences lessened during the 1920s and 1930s, and in the Second World War Kawanishi "developed excellent and original engineering techniques, which helped account for their success."[28]

Early in 1927 Kármán left Kobe for Vaals, leaving an assistant in charge of tunnel construction. Work continued throughout the year and ended in 1928. Coincidently, GALCIT's wind tunnel and laboratories required about the same gestation period after Kármán's initial pollination. The Guggenheim Building housing GALCIT—rising to five stories and measuring 160 by 55 feet—proved to be an impressive, state-of-the-art aeronautical center. Workmen fitted its wind tunnel with a 750-horsepower motor, attached by a driveshaft to a 15-foot propeller. At one end of the tunnel, in a room four stories high by 50 by 20 feet, models up to 30 feet in length would be subjected to air speeds stronger than 200 miles per hour. In the basement, a water channel 140 feet long, 10 feet deep, and 10 feet in width would allow research on seaplane and ship hulls. The first and second floors contained a machine shop, a motor-testing facility, six small laboratories for engine studies, and a huge wood shop to fabricate life-sized aircraft replicas. The third floor housed five offices, a drafting room, a seminar room, and a library. When the Guggenheim Laboratory opened its doors in fall 1928, a truly well-equipped aeronautical research institution went into operation.[29]

The unveiling was preceded by Kármán's return to Pasadena that September to undertake a final inspection of the tunnel. He and Clark Millikan had written frequently to one another during the construction of the GALCIT structure, a correspondence significant for its unmistakable tone of a boss instructing a subordinate. Kármán also visited Pasadena in the fall 1928 semester to honor an agreement made with Robert Millikan early in 1927. The arrangement allowed Paul Epstein and Kármán to exchange teaching positions one in every four terms. Epstein launched the swap at Aachen in fall 1927 and Kármán, now a GALCIT research associate, reciprocated the following year. It also gave the Hungarian a chance to participate in Cal Tech's efforts to organize a formal two-year postgraduate course in aeronautical engineering. But Robert Millikan had more important things in mind. On December 6, 1928, he cornered his guest while he was making a last assessment of the wind tunnel. They spoke privately for a few minutes, and the Cal Tech leader finally posed the big question: would Kármán become the GALCIT director?

He deferred an answer for the moment. Professor William F. Durand, chairman of the mechanical engineering department of Stanford University, had recently asked Kármán to become his successor.[30] But Durand's proposal held little appeal. Kármán still wanted advancement in Europe, although he now knew this could be a false hope. Ever since his return to Aachen after the war, the path to eminence had been blocked by Ludwig Prandtl. In 1921 he overlooked Kármán and chose Max Born for a chair in experimental physics at Göttingen. Then, between 1922 and 1925, while Prandtl negotiated with the Munich Polytechnic Institute for the directorship of its aeronautics school, Kármán was told not to expect to succeed his mentor. If Prandtl went to Munich, his old post would be converted to a junior position in physics. The reason probably involved birthright rather than qualifications. Göttingen already employed four distinguished Jewish scientists—Max Born, James Franck, Edmund Landau, and Richard Courant—and it was made clear that no more would be hired. In a highly nationalistic Germany, Kármán's Hungarian origins also worked against him. Even Born, his old roommate at Göttingen, failed to plead his case, fearing reprisals from his colleagues. In any event, Prandtl remained in Göttingen after being named director of its new hydrodynamics institute in 1925.

European economic conditions also conspired against the Aachen leader. German hyper-inflation during the 1920s reduced his institute's modest financial support and resulted in a disastrous decline in enrollment. In the math and physics departments, ninety-four students attended during the 1921 and 1922 semesters; only twenty-nine remained during 1924 and 1925. Göttingen, endowed heavily by the state and patronized by wealthier families, also suffered a decline, but not nearly as sharp as Aachen's. As a result, Kármán was forced to concentrate on the institute's solvency, leaving less time for his own research. Thus, such formidable obstacles as anti-Semitism, his nationality, the German economic crisis, and Prandtl's personal antipathy deterred Kármán from realizing the success he felt he had earned.[31]

Yet, these factors did not really clarify his response to Millikan's offer. The Hungarian had experienced bitter disappointment in Germany. But would he give up all hope and make the irrevocable decision to move his family to America? Not yet in 1928. Kármán rejected Durand's position without hesitation, confiding in Millikan that if he came to America, he would live only in Pasadena. The Cal Tech proposition could not be so readily dismissed. Kármán relished the thought of teaching in the United States because it presented a fresh venue for his ideas. He saw an almost singlehanded opportunity to awaken American aviation to the relationship between theoretical aerodynamics and practical aircraft design, a chance to implant the concept of engineering optimization to improve aeronautical performance. On the other hand, Helen von Kármán, now 76 years of age, rigidly opposed the Cal Tech option. She held patrician notions of the New World as a land populated by Old World misfits. She feared the ocean voyage and apparently had little regard for Robert Millikan. Pipö urged her brother to try Aachen once more. Even his colleagues argued against emigration, reminding him that at age 47, adaptation would be hard, especially in light of the lower social standing of university professors in America. Before returning to Aachen early in 1929, Kármán gently rebuffed—but did not reject—Millikan's proposal.[32]

But back at the Technical University, he started to rethink things. He noticed almost immediately after returning an upsurge of Nazi sentiment in Germany. He also began to detect it on campus. One of his most devoted pupils appeared in class with a swastika in the buttonhole of his coat. A Hungarian graduate student became embroiled in a dispute with a fraternity and found himself referred to as a "Hungarian Semite." In summer 1929 the institute hosted an international conference on aeronautics and inaugurated a new wing dedicated to supersonic aerodynamics. Kármán was in Kobe when the program was prepared. Unfortunately, the meetings occurred during the anniversary of the signing of the hated Treaty of Versailles, called the "Day of Mourning" in Germany. In an act sure to inflame passions, the proceedings included the award of honorary degrees to scientists from England and France, the victorious allies of World War I. Student protesters decried scheduling of a conference during the period of remembrance, and even more vigorously denounced giving honors to wartime enemies on the anniversary day. The rector of Aachen struck the degrees from the ceremonies, accepting the students' claim that only foreigners such as Kármán—not "real Germans"—would plan such an event. "Exceedingly angry" at this rebuke, the aeronautics director accused the rector of cowardice in the face of student pressure. Ultimately, the recipients received their diplomas, but in private ceremonies.

Coupled to these nationalist incidents, the Hungarian found disturbing signs of secret German rearmament. A Ministry of Transportation official from Berlin suggested he ask no questions when industrial firms sought to use the Aachen wind tunnel for high-speed tests. A former assistant died in an air crash after practicing high-speed rolling maneuvers, an event undoubtedly related to military tests. Kármán realized "the much discussed illegal army of Germany . . . was a reality, and . . . had a terrible foreboding for the future."[33] His mistreatment by Prandtl and Göttingen during the 1920s only deepened his fears.

While life began to look less happy at Aachen, Robert Millikan set every trap in his arsenal to catch Kármán. The day in December 1928 that he made the initial offer, the Cal Tech chief wrote to Harry Guggenheim asking for additional support to accomplish the deed. He reiterated the importance of bringing Kármán to GALCIT on a permanent basis, quoting Paul Epstein's observation that "no man [in the U.S.] . . . is in his class in his knowledge and grasp of the whole field, or would be of more outstanding importance for our country-wide aeronautical development if he could be intimately and fully identified with it."[34] How to "intimately and fully" identify him with Cal Tech became the question. Millikan faced obstacles of salary and research budgets, but Harry Guggenheim urged him to hire the man he really wanted and worry about cost later.

Undeterred by Kármán's initial reluctance, Millikan wrote him on the first of March, 1929, and again held out the appointment. Luckily, the candidate did not grasp it immediately. In spring, events overtook Millikan's second offer. During the past three years, University of Akron president George F. Zook had repeatedly solicited the Guggenheims to allocate $250,000 for an airship institute at his school. Suddenly, early in 1929, Zook won over his patrons. He also persuaded Professor Jerome C. Hunsaker of the Goodyear-Zeppelin Corporation and MIT to lead the project. But Harry Guggenheim had other plans. Akron should not control the institute, nor should Zook's candidate direct it. After discussions with Robert Millikan and Jerome Hunsaker in June, the philanthropist decided to forge a joint venture between GALCIT and Akron, renewable at the end of five years. Cal Tech would supply a research center and access to a potential dirigible hub in Southern California; Akron, home of Goodyear, would provide the industrial base.

Most important, Theodore von Kármán was nominated to be director of the new Daniel Guggenheim Airship Institute, a position he could oversee from Pasadena. To defray expenses, GALCIT would receive $75,000 from the grant over five years: a $10,000 per annum fellowship fund; $2,000 annual salary for Kármán; and $3,000 a year for miscellaneous costs. Thus, Harry Guggenheim gave Zook his institute, but used it to sweeten the incentives for Kármán's leap to America.

News of the agreement quickly reached Paul Epstein, on a visit to Aachen, and he again acted as Millikan's ambassador. Epstein posed the new proposition to his friend, and for the first time in the long affair, acceptance seemed likely. Together, GALCIT and the airship institute appeared sufficient to induce the Hungarian to settle in Southern California. This Kármán confirmed in a telegram in early July, raising the possibility of teaching at GALCIT in spring 1930.[35]

Millikan pressed the advantage. He sent a formal salary proposal: $10,000 a year to direct GALCIT, $2,000 for the airship institute. This represented three times his earnings at Aachen. Harry Guggenheim followed Millikan's figures with a more emotional appeal. He reminded Kármán that in America he would achieve immediate fame as the leader of the nation's aerodynamics scientists and engineers, find himself relieved of the heavy burden of consultative work, and enjoy the opportunity to contribute to a growing region of the country and a great school of science. Liberated from the constraints of fundraising, Kármán would be free to open more scholarly vistas than ever before. Any lingering doubts about adequate backing vanished in mid-October 1929 when Millikan promised an annual GALCIT budget of at least $50,000, under the director's personal control.

All these blandishments, as well as repeated assurances from Epstein and Millikan that his family would be greeted warmly in Pasadena, persuaded Kármán to take the big gamble. Last-minute efforts by the Prussian Ministry of Education failed to establish a second professorship in aeronautics at Aachen or to open a chair for him at the University of Berlin. The fall of the American stock market had brought economic paralysis to Germany and retrenchment everywhere. In fact, the salary of Prussian professors fell 15 percent. On October 20, 1929, Kármán wired Millikan to expect him in Pasadena in April 1930. By now, Pipö accepted the move. At first, his mother "refused to budge." But she slowly reconciled herself in order to see to her son's needs and to assist him with her fine command of English.

Kármán asked Frank Wattendorf to act as his representative in California and sent him ahead to Cal Tech. In December 1929 the three Kármáns walked up the gangway of an oceanliner bound for New York. Consoled for the moment by the prospect of a return for summer teaching—Kármán left Aachen on a leave of absence—they realized the voyage would alter their lives profoundly.[36]

CHAPTER 4

# A Magnet for Aeronautics

For the third time in three years, Theodore von Kármán rode the rails from New York to Los Angeles. This time, though, he faced the immediate prospect of setting up a household. Fortunately, the real estate listings around Cal Tech showed one home that appealed to mother, son, and sister. Located two miles from the campus at 1501 South Marengo Avenue, it stood on a lot at the southern extreme of Pasadena, almost straddling the borders of San Marino and Los Angeles. The home had ample space and two acres of lovely grounds. Its sweeping front lawn, heavy tiled roof, low stucco walls, and winding garden paths recalled a Spanish villa. The interior had large public rooms on the first floor and three bedrooms upstairs. Kármán liked the added luxury of a dressing room adjacent to his own. For work at home, he converted a downstairs room into a study. "The house," observed a former student, "was not one a wealthy American would live in; [rather, it was] a rambling, European style house."[1]

In the weeks and months ahead, as the family unpacked and furnished the home, the lure of Aachen diminished as the routine of the new life took hold. Helen von Kármán quickly relinquished her harsh judgments of America. Once she got to know it, "she liked [the country] very much." Kármán himself sensed almost from the beginning that he had made a wise choice. He received from colleagues and students a degree of friendship and admiration unknown in Aachen. His salary ranked third among all Cal Tech employees. While the GALCIT director did return to the Technical University during summer 1930, visits the following two years became more perfunctory. Writing to Ludwig Prandtl, he could not resist chuckling about his decision to emigrate.

> I got a short letter from Berlin suggesting that I take up my activities over there in the fall. I do not think I will do this; I find my situation here quite

satisfactory. The German academic life has some advantages, for instance a definitely better beer than here, but I think you will agree with me that this is not sufficient reason for me to neglect the disadvantages.[2]

The factors of home, family, personal relations, and salary all contributed to Kármán's growing allegiance to Pasadena. But none of these attractions counted more than his absorption in the life of GALCIT. Millikan made clear to him just what Cal Tech expected from the Guggenheim Laboratory—a vehicle to draw the U.S. aviation industry to Southern California and to bring to the campus national preeminence in aeronautics. These expectations were first answered by the publication of an "Announcement of the Graduate School of Aeronautics." Issued the month after Kármán and his family arrived, it gave the first clear sign of the direction he would lead GALCIT. Bateman, Klein, and Clark Millikan still formed the core of the regular faculty. Arthur E. Raymond (assistant chief engineer of Douglas Aircraft) and Ernest E. Sechler (a doctoral candidate) acted as adjuncts. These men received part-time assistance from Paul Epstein, fellow mathematician Eric Temple Bell, and professor of geophysics Beno Gutenberg. If the faculty remained much the same since the opening of GALCIT, two main interests now dominated its curriculum: aeronautical structures (elasticity) and aerodynamics (fluid mechanics).[3]

These academic emphases reflected Theodore von Kármán's passion for applying theoretical research to practical problems, as well as Robert Millikan's ambitions for regional aviation. The structural program sought consciously to provide aircraft companies with reliable data on metal skins and supports based upon "sound theory . . . substantiated by experimental evidence." Raymond and Klein taught the elasticity courses while Kármán, interested in columnar strength since his youth, developed theories on the buckling properties of sheet metals. The aerodynamics program, on the other hand, concentrated on skin friction and boundary layer phenomena, exploring fundamental concepts of aerodynamic drag both in the GALCIT wind tunnel and on test aircraft. Kármán, Klein, and Clark Millikan were the mainstays of this faction, pursuing wing theory and new frontiers of fluid mechanics.

In short order, the results flowing from the GALCIT laboratory influenced the design of the latest aircraft produced by such Pacific coast firms as Douglas, Lockheed, Consolidated-Vultee, North American, Boeing, Hughes, and Curtiss-Wright. In fact, a hint of the coming success occurred just after Kármán assumed control of the lab. Original plans divided access to the wind tunnel equally among GALCIT researchers and the regional aircraft industries. But since this was one of the highest performance wind tunnels in existence, the proportion gradually shifted toward the commercial firms. Indeed, it became so popular that in spite of seventeen-hour-a-day operations, lab personnel could find only a few weeks a year for their own work.

The heavy booking may be explained in part by the labor-intensive nature of the experiments. Most took from one to four weeks. The manufacturers delivered large hardwood models of their prototype aircraft to the lab. Teams of part-time GALCIT students then undertook all the necessary tests. They suspended the wooden dummies—some with eight- to nine-foot wing spans—from seven balance points and subjected them to a variety of air speeds. Weight readings taken at the seven terminals, relayed to two operators in a control room, indicated the load carried by the models at various altitudes and velocities. The data were then compared by the staff to aerodynamic calculations. Clark Millikan analyzed the findings and prepared reports for the companies, often suggesting improvements in the prototype designs.[4]

The magnificent Guggenheim wind tunnel allowed Kármán and Millikan the opportunity to diagnose flight characteristics of aircraft in the early stages of development. With the help of Arthur Klein, they conceived a means of satisfying the three main concerns of aviation designers: the aircraft efficiency factor, expressed in lift versus drag; the minimization of drag; and the maximization of lift. Kármán and his colleagues believed they could accurately predict overall aerodynamic performance by wind tunnel experimentation (although they admitted this applied more to glide conditions than powered flight). Drag could be determined through calculations based upon hydrodynamic theories of skin friction pioneered at GALCIT. Finally, lift factors were accounted for after intense mathematical study of the transition from laminar to turbulent flow, tested by artificial turbulence in the tunnel.

For the first time in America, a flight dynamics scholar of international renown invited leaders of the aircraft industry to derive practical benefits from his research. Engineers employed by local manufacturers appeared at GALCIT not just to observe the wind tunnel, but to attend the director's lectures on the science of aeronautics. Once they realized the increases in aircraft efficiency to be derived from such studies, the boards of Douglas, Northrop, and Lockheed began to hire GALCIT aerodynamics graduates as full-time members of their staffs. Other companies followed their example. As a consequence, in a relatively short period of time the empirical design of aircraft gave way to a scientifically based approach to materials, shapes, and structures.

No GALCIT project promoted the cause of wind tunnel research—or, indeed, of aeronautical science—quite like the famous Douglas Commercial (DC) aircraft. The initial contact occurred between Arthur Klein and Donald Douglas. Klein worked on a part-time basis for the Santa Monica airplane manufacturer and persuaded him to refer some of his technical problems to the Pasadena campus. Though underwritten at first by the Guggenheims, the design work undertaken for Douglas eventually led to a booming consultancy for GALCIT and its wind tunnel. Interest in passenger planes quickened in February 1934, when the U.S. Army Air Corps abruptly canceled its airmail contracts with private carriers and began to fly the routes with military vehicles and crews. Deprived of lucrative orders for transport aircraft, Douglas frantically sought alternatives and asked Cal Tech's Arthur Raymond to help him find a niche in commercial aviation. The result was the DC-1, built for the speed and comfort of the flying public, rather than for sacks of letters. The DC-2 enlarged on the Raymond airplane.

But the renowned DC-3, empress of American and world air travel, attained its legendary status in part because of advice rendered by Kármán and his staff to the Douglas engineers. In flight tests, the DC-3 prototype experienced severe wind buffeting, particularly serious due to its low-fuselage wing mounting. Through calculations and experimentation, Kármán found a thin fairing (or fillet), placed along the juncture of the fuselage and upper wing, quieted the turbulence. Wind tunnel data proved this technique eliminated a dangerous leading edge, from which eddies of air (the notorious Kármán vortices) shot back, severely shaking the aircraft's rear structure. The discovery made the difference between a highly stable plane and one threatened by the dangerous turbulence associated with many other transports. In France, engineers soon spoke of these amazingly simple but effective fillets as "Kármáns," a feature that found its way into countless aeronautical designs.

One other Cal Tech innovation greatly improved the seminal DC-3. Until the early 1930s, airplane fabrication principally relied on wood and fabric construction. Industries shied away from metal structures and skins, fearing the weight and buckling qualities rendered it unsafe for the pressures associated with flight. But Kármán, working with Ernest Sechler, proved on paper and in the lab that by running stiffeners along its surfaces, sheet metal would flex, not deform. Built entirely of these materials, the DC-3 began regular service in 1935, an event that greatly popularized these new methods among other manufacturers. The outstanding successes of the fillets and the monocoque (load-bearing) fuselage improved the efficiency of the Douglas aircraft and set GALCIT on the course envisioned by Robert A. Millikan: an intellectual beacon for a powerful, regional aviation industry.[5]

During this period, the director of the Guggenheim Lab not only put Pasadena on the map, but devoted much of his considerable energies to the airship institute at Akron. Despite some important discoveries on dirigible design, the Ohio center never achieved the prominence of its Cal Tech counterpart. Kármán assumed the role of director in September 1930 and selected one of his senior assistants at Aachen, Dr. Theodore Troller, to supervise the construction of the Akron facilities. Starting in January 1931, Troller, Hans Bücken (another designer from the Technical University), and Frank Wattendorf (sent by Kármán to advise on aerodynamics) oversaw the building of a four-story structure in a corner of the Akron Municipal Airport. The centerpiece of the institute—a 6½-foot vertical wind tunnel—began operations in May 1932. Troller assumed the title of resident director and on June 26, 1932, Dr. Zook, Robert Millikan, and Jerome Hunsaker presided over the opening of the institute. The Akron president spoke expansively of regular, two-day dirigible transit across the Atlantic. The Cal Tech leader predicted four-day service from Los Angeles to Tokyo.[6]

Theodore von Kármán loved the grace and practicality of airships, but he also knew their inherent aeronautical weaknesses. Their enormous, lightweight structures sometimes fell victim to dangerous instability in flight. In 1925 the first rigid U.S. dirigible, the *Shenandoah,* broke apart in a storm over Ohio, killing fourteen. Congress then approved funds to erect two larger and stronger vessels, the *Macon* and *Akron.* The two behemoths, constructed for the U.S. Navy just as Kármán's airship institute geared up for operations, might have profited from the research of Troller and his colleagues. In April 1933, the *Akron* was torn asunder by violent storms over the Atlantic Ocean, resulting in the deaths of seventy-three passengers and crew. Investigating the incident, Kármán brought to bear two important ingredients: an appreciation for the influence of weather and an understanding of the air resistance acting on the massive hulls. A young Cal Tech meteorologist named Irving Krick attributed the *Akron*'s demise to the collision of two powerful air masses directly in the dirigible's path. Kármán helped publicize this hypothesis. The GALCIT chief also demonstrated mathematically, and confirmed in wind tunnel experiments, a general formula for the skin friction of smooth surfaces, suggesting new designs to enable the vulnerable giants to endure the heavy, turbulent fronts found over the Atlantic.

Before tests could be undertaken on Kármán's new configurations, in February 1935 the *Akron*'s sister ship also fell from the sky. The bigger *Macon* tumbled into the Pacific Ocean off Point Sur, California, after a gust of wind ripped the top fin from its frame. Although only two died this time, public confidence in airships collapsed. Again, Irving Krick found the culprit in the weather—a hidden wall of turbulence called an occluded front. But Kármán felt the broader failure of the airships stemmed from insufficient theoretical and experimental knowledge of the forces acting on them during flight. In fact, explanations no longer mattered. President Franklin D. Roosevelt openly questioned their airworthiness and a Navy Special Committee on Airships, on which the Hungarian sat, chastised the service for complacency in building and operating dirigibles without adequate prior testing. Kármán read the public mood clearly and finally admitted that, in their existing state, the big airborne ships could not be relied on to survive the punishment of Atlantic crossings and provide economical transport. Consequently, when Cal Tech's five-year commitment to the airship institute ended in October 1934, Harry Guggenheim, Robert Millikan, and Theodore von Kármán agreed to transfer full control to Dr. Troller and the University of Akron.[7]

Despite the disappointments of dirigible research, Kármán's analyses did not lie fallow. They led him back again to the study of turbulence, which he had wrestled with at the applied mechanics conferences at Innsbruck (1922) and Delft (1924). Kármán brought a good deal of humility to the subject, imparted by Arthur Sommerfeld, the noted German physicist. Sommerfeld once told him that there were only two scientific processes he really wanted to understand: the basis of quantum theory, and the true meaning of turbulence. "If I have to die," said Sommerfeld, "I hope that my creator will explain . . . quantum theory, [because] turbulence is so difficult, . . . even the good lord [himself] cannot explain it!"[8] Elusive theoretically, turbulent motion accounted for many tangible effects. It increased frictional resistance, heat transfer, and the diffusion of fluids, and acted as a serious impediment to improvements in aeronautical design. Though defined as the *irregular* motion of gases or fluids past stationary objects, it occurred more commonly in nature than smooth flow. Kármán sought to learn about and predict the random movement of particles through fundamental, statistical laws.[9]

Prandtl's boundary layer theory afforded a clue to unraveling the mystery. Despite the wide array of turbulence in the atmosphere, the laminar flow of air over an aircraft wing remained largely unaffected by the turmoil around it. This suggested a mathematical solution to turbulent activity. If laminar flow could be represented as parallel columns of soldiers, turbulent flow could be represented by an equal number marching perpendicular to the double rows. The friction encountered as the soldiers clashed would slow the progress of the forward-moving columns. But if all the men moved at equal intervals over equal distances, elemental laws of probability could be brought to bear on this apparent chaos. Just as soldiers collided in this example, layers of gases likewise passed over one another, causing friction at the molecular level. Ludwig Prandtl announced this principle at the 1926 Congress of Applied Mechanics held at Zurich. His "Mixing Length Concept" accurately predicted the distance molecules traveled before impacting other molecules, thus losing momentum. It marked an important step toward a fuller understanding of chaotic motion.[10]

Even though the next four years took Theodore von Kármán farther and farther from the orbit of Göttingen, he could not resist the old instinct to compete with—and, if possible, surpass—his mentor. A "formidable opponent," Prandtl developed his theories with great care. He had at his disposal years of experimental data gathered on such diverse phenomena as the velocity, flow, and pressure of air and water moving both in straight tracks and curved surfaces. Kármán's mentor always accompanied theory with experiments, and both were developed with painstaking attention to detail. The GALCIT director admired this process, but did not have the staff, time, or the patience for such work. As in the past, he would search his mind for an intuitive insight to push him through the empirical morass. In his race to best Prandtl in the "Olympic Games" for a universal law of turbulence, he had a clear deadline. The Fourth Congress of Applied Mechanics would be held in

August 1930 in Stockholm. He knew Prandtl was straining toward the same end; both men had been invited to present papers on turbulence.

For the battle, Kármán recruited Frank Wattendorf, who had studied turbulent motion at Göttingen during the Hungarian's first journey to the United States. Wattendorf had obtained some published and unpublished experimental data from Prandtl and began to plot the numbers, hoping they would assume a straight line, the shape of mathematical law. Kármán and his pupil often pondered the problem late into the evening. One such night in Vaals, the Aachen professor found the "happy thought" he had spoken of in 1924. A formula slowly began to fall into place which both explained the experimental data and satisfied his theoretical concept. They struggled on until just before midnight, when Wattendorf, noting the approaching hour, dashed out to meet the last streetcar running to his home in Aachen. Following in close pursuit, Kármán suddenly saw the final equations flash in his mind. Having no other place to write, he scratched the formula on the exterior of trolley number 12. The conductor at first watched this odd scene with patience. But after more delay he started to glance nervously at his watch. He coughed gently. Finally, he gestured sharply to Wattendorf to climb aboard as he eased the lever activating the train. Kármán's colleague plunged into the moving car just as his mentor finished the last furious notations on its side. At every stop on the homeward trip, Wattendorf jumped out to copy a few lines of the scrawl, and stepped in as the train rolled on. He took down the last bit just as he reached his destination and hurried home to reduce the equations to elemental form. The results explained all of the figures he had plotted earlier.[11]

Kármán knew he had beaten Prandtl and exulted in the victory. Nonetheless, the Stockholm conference was still months off and as his old teacher had generously opened his experimental notebooks to Wattendorf, Kármán decided to warn him of the discovery before the meeting. Prandtl graciously invited him to present his results at the Göttingen Scientific Society, the site of Kármán's vortex triumph. Entitled "Mechanical Similarity in Turbulence," he approached the mixing length concept from a wider viewpoint than Prandtl. He assumed the flow patterns of any two adjacent points in a turbulent system to be similar, differing only in length and time frame. Through specific differential equations, Kármán showed the distance to collision (mixing length) to be proportional to the velocity distribution of the points in chaos. Called logarithmic velocity distribution after its method of calculation, Kármán found it agreed "very well" with experimental measurements of the phenomena. In short, he had uncovered a valid engineering formula for forces of skin friction and, more fundamentally, found "a form of predictable order in the randomness of turbulent motion."[12]

Prandtl reacted to the paper with ambivalence. Proud of his student, he nonetheless bristled at being overtaken in a field in which he had made such profound contributions. Prandtl withdrew his presentation from the Stockholm program, leaving the spotlight to Kármán. But the race lingered on; who would be the first to prove the theory experimentally? As soon as he settled in Pasadena, Kármán contacted Dr. Hugh Dryden of the National Bureau of Standards, an expert on anemometers. These instruments measured changes in the speed of the wind, as well as patterns of turbulent motion. Dryden sent his assistant, Arnold Kuethe, to GALCIT, where he joined Frank Wattendorf in the search for proof of the skin friction hypothesis. Day after day Kármán visited the third-floor lab and cheered Wattendorf and Kuethe as they struggled to prove the theory. In the meantime, Prandtl and his colleagues proceeded on a similar course. Finally, Wattendorf appeared at Marengo Avenue with exciting news: reliable test results had started to materialize. After some initial miscalculations, the magical straight line appeared as the two men plotted the data. "It meant," Kármán later remembered, "confirmation of what I intuitively always believed; [a] correlation among the turbulent fluctuations and the evidence that order existed in the internal mechanism of turbulence."[13] The day after the results were confirmed, Kármán read the findings at a conference of the newly formed Institute of Aeronautical Sciences in New York. It appeared as the lead article in the first issue of the *Journal of the Institute of Aeronautical Sciences.*[14]

Theodore von Kármán's law of turbulence exerted far-reaching effects on the design of airships, high-speed aircraft, and rockets. Just as important for U.S. aviation, its publication represented a critical turning point in his career. It marked an end of the long, sometimes bitter competition with Prandtl. By ending this contest, Kármán could concentrate his mind fully on Pasadena. He still loved Aachen and thought nostalgically of his life there. Indeed, during his first five years in America he spent much of his time completing scientific problems begun at the Technical University. But after 1935—after GALCIT had been well established and after the duel with Prandtl had finally subsided—Kármán embarked on a new phase of his career, one centered fully in the present rather than the past, one centered in America rather than Europe.

If Kármán had fully set his mind on an American life by the mid-1930s, he acted on his intentions on July 24, 1936, taking the oath of citizenship in the U.S. District Court of Los Angeles. By this time, his teaching and research revolved around the duality of home and office. Indeed, he conducted as much of his professional activities in the company of his mother and sister as in the laboratories of GALCIT. The polarity followed the pattern of Vaals, substituting automobiles for trolleys, and sleepy Pasadena for the more lively Aachen. As in Holland, his private residence—the place where he imparted knowledge in a relaxed, friendly atmosphere—became the cradle of teaching and learning at the Guggenheim Laboratory.

The house on South Marengo Avenue suited this purpose admirably. Not a mansion in size or elegance, its rambling Mediterranean layout, wrapped around a tiled central courtyard, nonetheless disguised a home of deceptively fine style. By the mid-1930s, Kármán, Josephine, and his mother had furnished it in a comfortable, informal manner. Every room held a crazy quilt of furniture and accessories, suggesting occupants of international taste and travel. To first-time visitors the home made a warm, welcoming (if somewhat cluttered) impression. From the broad foyer, guests either walked into a cavernous living room on the left, or into an impressive dining room of great length on the right. Below the high, beamed ceilings ran banks of tall, heavily draped windows.

Once they entered, the many students, colleagues, and friends of the GALCIT chief noticed a patchwork of Persian, Turkish, and Chinese rugs; a number of large Chinese and Japanese floor screens; small sofas and many side chairs upholstered in Japanese silk; and in every possible space an assortment of Chinese and Japanese stands, curios, tables, potteryware, dolls, wall scrolls, plaques, figurines, and vases. In addition, scattered trophies, books, papers, honorary degrees, and innumerable family photographs of all sizes filled the public part of the home. Much of the charm of 1501 South Marengo was smelled rather than seen. In a big, square, spartanly furnished kitchen, Pipö and Mrs. von Kármán, and on occasion a cook, worked over a large O'Keefe and Merritt gas range to prepare rich Hungarian foods for the never-ending stream of visitors.[15]

The people who arrived at the door came mainly for a taste of the famous Kármán persona. It imbued the house with a special personality. On days off from Cal Tech, he awoke at 6 A.M. and after eating breakfast, sometimes with guests, dictated correspondence and read bundles of mail from former pupils and fellow scientists. The telephone rang unceasingly. At lunch he usually entertained more visitors, with whom he always enjoyed a shot of Jack Daniel's whisky or some Hungarian plum brandy. After resting from three to five in the afternoon, he rose for the evening's activities. First he lit a fat black cigar and poured another Jack Daniel's, both of which were replenished throughout the evening. Then Kármán enjoyed a large dinner. Around eight the doorbell announced the first of a procession of callers-by. The amazingly diverse parade of Hungarian emigrés, Hollywood movie stars, priests, colonels, businessmen, artists, musicians, philosophers, writers, and scientists called at his home not so much to discover the secrets of flight as to enjoy his exuberant outlook.

As Kármán himself joked, his most difficult adjustment in America involved learning English. But he turned this weakness into a strength, a point of charm. Hugh Dryden, his friend from the National Bureau of Standards, thought Kármán's melodious baritone accent had been fabricated for "commercial purposes." Because of the Hungarian habit of accentuating the first syllable of words, one ticket agent at a New York railway station sold Kármán a fare to Kansas City after hearing his request for "Schenectady." Uninitiated students often wondered why he talked so much about "cows" in his lecture on turbulence; of course, he meant "chaos." His Hungaro-English also had a uniquely personal sound because of serious deafness in his left ear. The GALCIT director always wore a hearing aid and often answered questions with a little more mysteriousness than his listeners expected. But even this fact failed to deter his visitors.

His looks and manner complemented his voice. Uniquely attractive, he was five feet eight inches tall, had wavy gray hair, a sizable aquiline nose, sparkling grey eyes, and a half-smiling, lively expression. He looked about fifteen years younger than his true age. There was an aspect of shyness in his manner, characterized by a gentle shrugging of the shoulders as he spoke. The hands, which habitually sliced and swept the air, always accompanied his discourse. During parties, the gestures often punctuated earthy jokes. His memory for anecdote equaled his childhood recall of numbers, and he could quickly call up stories suited to whatever the situation demanded. Kármán's attraction also sprang from the intense focus of his mind. He communicated as if nothing mattered but the person before him. The host of Marengo Avenue effortlessly adjusted his conversation to the tastes of his listeners, never leaving the impression of a great man uttering lofty thoughts. He felt that station in life meant little; shared experience meant a great deal. Finally, Kármán adored women, especially beautiful ones. At all parties, he ambled toward them with the full determination of an Hungarian bachelor, embracing them, speaking to them in intimate confidence. Much more often than not, they loved his attentions as much as he loved their company.[16]

The two "steady" women of the house, of course, were his sister and his mother. The guests may have come to see her son, but Mrs. von Kármán—who shared the stage with Koko, the big, black family poodle whom Kármán loved and who trailed him everywhere—held sway over the throngs.[17] Seated in the living room on a throne-like chair, this tiny person with the good English presided over the household. A "marvelous" woman of keen humor and intelligence, she must have been the source of her son's fantastic memory. The wives of students often introduced themselves to her somewhat timidly, afraid she might not remember them from past visits. The old woman not only recalled details of their previous conversations, but recited exactly what they had worn on their previous meeting! His pupils relished this sympathetic, grandmotherly figure because, as her son realized, she represented "an example of an old lady who does not want to be young." More important, she always asked them whether Todor had demanded too much in or out of class.[18]

Kármán's attachment to his mother may have been deep, but his emotional life centered on his "darling little sister," Josephine. With her he enjoyed an especially profound and chaste bond. Like their mother, she was a woman of significant accomplishments. She earned a doctorate in the history of art, taught French at the University of Southern California, and wrote a book on early Christian antiquities. Pipö played a crucial part in Kármán's career. She inspired her brother to commit himself to countless "international, scientific, and social activities" and he attributed much of his success to her wise counsel. She also contributed greatly to the happy, salon-like atmosphere of the home, connecting her brother to the Los Angeles Hungarian community (including actors Paul Lukas, Jolie Gabor, and Illona Massey).

But such intense devotion also carried with it a negative quality. She exercised a strongly proprietary control over his time and attention. Moreover, some of Kármán's friends and students felt she bullied him into unnecessary social engagements. They found her self-centered and domineering. Despite the many public occasions on which he acknowledged her contributions to the quiet life necessary for his work, such critics believed he achieved all he did *in spite of* her continuous interruptions and diversions. Yet, Kármán's devotion to her ran just as strongly as hers to him. Pipö once accused a hairdresser of stealing some of her jewelry. Kármán's students believed Josephine had really lost the pieces herself and blamed the woman to cover her mistake. But to Theodore, there could be no doubt. Some time after the incident, his old friend Arthur Klein remarked casually that he, too, found it hard to believe Pipö's story. When the Hungarian learned about the comment, he cut off all personal communications with Klein. Henceforth, the two spoke only on a professional basis. Such was the relationship with Pipö; the usually good-humored Kármán would not tolerate the slightest criticism of his sister.[19]

Despite this one area of friction, the Kármán home held a wonderful attraction to his many friends. Yet it represented not just pleasure, but work as well. "The Boss," as his pupils and associates liked to call him, often told them to bring along their scientific problems to the Marengo Avenue parties. But if they appeared on the tiled courtyard outside Kármán's big front door expecting to begin their tutorial promptly, they had a strange surprise in store. Greeted loudly by their professor with a shout of their name and an expression of delight, he conducted them into a living room teeming with men and women of a dozen professions, from a dozen countries. Kármán no sooner deposited these innocents in the midst of the hard-drinking, good-humored crowd than he vanished temporarily with several others out the kitchen door and into a small study located in a cottage at the rear of the house. Choked with cigar smoke, dominated by a large, carved mahogany desk and a very old semi-wing desk chair, it was the scene of thousands of rushed conferences between pupils and teacher. Across a wicker dinette table topped by glass they joked, quickly exchanged papers, scrawled out new equations, and discussed the solutions to some especially vexing problems.

Before an hour elapsed, Kármán would adjourn the meeting to greet new guests and see others off. Free to roam, the students ate heartily and drank whiskey or scotch for the rest of the night. Most of them and the other visitors said their goodbyes around midnight; the few who required more of the master's time retired back to the study. "Would you like to work now?" he asked, and for the next two hours gave them his undivided attention, kindled their enthusiasm, and filled sheets of scratch paper with calculations. Sometimes they awoke at 2 A.M. to hear the Boss throw his pencil on the desk after realizing some special mathematical triumph. "His teaching," remarked a former student, "was very personal, by no means confined to the classroom or restricted to scientific subjects."[20] Thus, Marengo Avenue provided the spiritual center of Kármán's life, a place where he conveyed important scientific and personal lessons to many academic disciples.

The regime at GALCIT, the other half of his life, involved a somewhat different flavor and routine than at home. Here the operation of the laboratory paced the interactions between teacher and students. While still working in a warm, friendly, and informal atmosphere, Kármán's young scholars found themselves in an environment in which they had to excel. At 1:30 in the afternoon every Tuesday, the director chaired a weekly departmental meeting known as the GALCIT Research Conferences. Out of respect, all rose when he entered the room. Cigar in one hand, gesturing animatedly with the other, Kármán began the sessions with a joke or funny observation and the smiling expression he assumed lasted throughout the meeting. The department secretary then recited the last week's minutes, after which every person present—Kármán himself, fellow faculty, visiting scholars, graduate students, and lab assistants—reported briefly on their projects. None dared let more than one conference pass without speaking. Kármán wanted open inquiry and dialogue to test and strengthen ideas, impossible if people failed to talk freely and expose errors and shortcomings to friendly criticism. His extraordinary memory often linked GALCIT work to parallel aeronautical research activities around the world. Staff members profited not just from each other's knowledge, but could also draw upon the Boss's international sources. Finally, to encourage discussion, Kármán dictated a one-sentence summary after each person described his weekly activities. All participants knew that the following Tuesday their remarks would be read aloud before their turn to speak.

Though rigorous, the research conferences had a pleasant and stimulating effect. The participants became excited about each other's discoveries and worked together to overcome obstacles. Kármán's infectious enthusiasm for problem solving and his visible delight in good answers encouraged everyone. Augmenting these meetings, the GALCIT weekly aeronautics seminar served as a colloquium to focus attention on topics of special interest. Clark Millikan scheduled guest speakers from the department and from the regional aircraft industries. They presented their most recent findings to the Guggenheim staff, as well as to visiting engineers from Douglas, Lockheed, and Boeing. Kármán's belief that ideas begat ideas—in sharp contrast to the proprietary view of scientific progress—informed the entire GALCIT operation.[21]

Teaching at the Guggenheim lab was more relaxed than these seminars might suggest. Since the institute never graduated more than a handful of students each year, Kármán's pupils learned in the tutorial method. If he walked by their offices and noticed someone struggling with an especially hard problem, he would sit down for a few moments and solve it, always in the trademark style of "beautiful, direct, highly geometrical reasoning." Or they might leave a series of frustrating equations on their desks overnight, only to find the answers the following morning written on the back of an envelope or a theater program in the even, calligraphic hand of the Boss. The only words left behind: "I think this is what you want!" Sometimes this impromptu tutoring occurred during conversation. One pupil told him of an experimental phenomenon he had observed but could not explain. Kármán suggested a plausible solution, and the young man turned away, satisfied. But the Hungarian stopped him; just in case the experimental data proved inaccurate, Kármán gave an equally likely explanation for the very opposite effect. Such private moments consumed so much of his time, he once found it necessary to hire a messenger service to warn him of impending lecture commitments![22]

Once he finally arrived in front of his classes, the students found the wait worthwhile. The sessions were always crowded and popular. Brilliant, unorthodox, yet "a very gentle teacher," the Boss never formally prepared these presentations, and never taught the same way twice. Indeed, Kármán frequently chose problems he had not fully considered, spontaneously working out analyses in beautiful rows of white symbols. Midway through such difficult calculations, he often stepped back from the blackboard, drew out a handkerchief from his pocket, placed one corner in his mouth, and twisted and chewed on it as he mentally pushed through to a solution. When he grasped the chalk again, the students observed in a flash the operation of his mind. His dexterity in extricating himself from these mathematical blind alleys often astounded the classes, which sometimes broke into applause at the mental manipulations performed before their eyes. Despite the appearance of showmanship, however, Kármán's lectures exhibited rare clarity and imagination, proceeding from the specific to the general. He presented problems with appealing simplicity, describing complex processes with common examples from daily life, often drawing word pictures. He spared his students the complications so they could grasp the fundamental principles.

Kármán's pupils treated him with great respect, addressing him always as Dr. von Kármán. Yet, in the Cal Tech tradition of informality, they felt free to interrupt his lectures to clarify points, which he answered patiently. During the first weeks of the semester, some of the young people found it hard to master his accent, more difficult still because of his impaired hearing. But most quickly got the idea. In spite of his mother's concern that Kármán not treat his pupils too rigorously, he established a loose regime in class: casual attire, no attendance taken, and tardiness excused. So long as they paid attention—those who failed in this respect might find a cup of black coffee brought to their seat in class—all went well. The grading also had a decidedly forgiving quality. Kármán disliked this aspect of teaching, and either asked one of his graduate students to assign marks or gave oral exams. So no one would fail, he often raised by one letter all grades assigned by his readers. One of his students became unnerved during his first oral exam (attended, as usual, by most of the faculty) and flunked it. But afterward, the professor put an arm around his shoulder, told him not to be discouraged, and passed him with a *C*. He later proved to be a star pupil.[23]

Kármán's tolerance and empathy for his protégés called forth a filial affection that lasted throughout their lives. The GALCIT director set two pedagogical objectives: give students his unstinting time and attention, and instill in them the importance of basic science to aeronautical engineering. He never accepted the American approach to college instruction, in which junior faculty or graduate assistants taught the undergraduates while the eminent tutored select graduate students. Based on the European model, he believed men of the highest stature should teach the most *elementary* classes. Just as he had learned the fundamentals of advanced mathematics from the great David Hilbert, American students should have the same opportunity to be grounded in their discipline by a master. In fact, Kármán argued that the lower-level courses demanded the greatest teaching: more clarity and less complication, the capacity to stimulate creative impulses, and an ability to impart a sense of the main principles involved.

But, Cal Tech, like most U.S. institutions of higher education, structured itself toward measurement of the student's curricular progress, rather than toward broad learning. Undergraduates took frequent tests, were assigned daily readings from textbooks, copied lecture notes slavishly, attended classes on a compulsory basis, and sat in small classes of twenty-five to thirty. Kármán observed that so long as the American method depended on external controls and the mastery of detail, there would never be enough distinguished professors to teach the basic courses. He experienced this frustrating situation himself. Even though he offered to instruct lower-division mathematics or aerodynamics courses, the administration always refused his suggestions.

Yet the Boss found means of circumventing the prevailing customs. He opened his home to break down barriers with his young charges. He tested his classes only once a semester, and handed out the questions in advance. He rewarded students who took novel approaches based on theoretical analyses, rather than those who submitted correct but uninspired work. Finally, to encourage imagination instead of mere repetition, he trained them to disregard artificial distinctions between aerodynamics and allied sciences. In order to make profound discoveries in aeronautics they needed to know the fundamentals of physics and chemistry and understand how the forces of nature interacted when flight occurred. Once they grasped the *principles,* the students could proceed to experimentation and the making of machines.[24]

By the mid-1930s, then, Theodore von Kármán had duplicated the successes he achieved at the Aachen Technical Institute. In a few short years he turned the fledgling GALCIT aeronautics program into one of the finest in America and a contender for international prominence. He established an enviable system of teaching and research. The wind tunnel's usefulness to the aircraft industry generated handsome revenues, funding salaries for visiting scholars, travel for GALCIT faculty, the finest equipment for the labs, and student fellowships and assistantships. "Go and buy it," Kármán often told Clark Millikan, "I'll find the money." Kármán's breakthroughs in turbulence theory carried the institute's name far and wide. The director quickly found himself at ease on the Pasadena campus, as well as at home. In essence, Robert A. Millikan's vision had been fulfilled.

As a crowning success, superb students enrolled at Cal Tech to study with Kármán. Reflecting a contentment with his adopted homeland, his favorites were the Americans. William R. Sears, Homer J.

Stewart, and Frank Marble all transferred from Midwest undergraduate programs in aeronautical engineering to study at GALCIT. Ernest Sechler, born in Colorado, took all his degrees at Cal Tech. But Frank J. Malina, a Texan who arrived in Pasadena in 1934 from Texas A&M University, made the greatest impact on Kármán.[25] The synergy between the middle-aged Hungarian and the young Texan would result in the transformation both of the highly successful GALCIT operation and of Kármán's professional interests.

CHAPTER 5

# The Rocketeers

Shortly after young men such as Malina, Sears, and the others began to arrive at GALCIT, Kármán found himself prepared to entertain new ventures. His style of leadership, called "seed spreading" by one associate, compelled him to start projects, only to leave them in the hands of others once they had been established. This he did in many instances: with Clark Millikan and the GALCIT wind tunnel; with Theodore Troller and the Akron Airship Institute; and with Leslie Howarth and C. C. Lin, two of his graduate students who carried forward his theory of turbulence. Kármán may have initiated the courting dance with the Southern California aviation industries, but William Sears consummated the relationship by becoming Northrop Aircraft's chief of aerodynamics. By 1935, then, the Boss looked for new grounds to scatter the germs of discovery. The search would lead him far afield.[1]

Just after World War I, American physicist Robert H. Goddard published a bold article entitled "A Method of Reaching Extreme Altitudes." His calculations plotted the trajectory of a long-range rocket capable of breaking through the earth's atmosphere and operating in the vacuum of space. Four years later, Transylvanian-born physicist and astronomer Hermann Oberth wrote "The Rocket into Interplanetary Space," a mathematical argument predicting projectiles that could be launched into orbit around the world. Oberth's preference for chemical propellants gained wide acceptance among those devoted to future space exploration. Nonetheless, in March 1926, Goddard, financed by the Smithsonian Institution, engineered the first flight of a liquid-fueled rocket engine.[2]

Still at the Technical University at Aachen, Kármán followed these events carefully. During the 1920s he heard Oberth lecture at a German aeronautics conference at Danzig. There the Romanian spoke enthusiastically of spaceships capable of escaping earth's gravitational pull. Kármán laughed a little at such adventurous talk, but admitted Oberth was persuasive; highly efficient fuels might well lift large vehicles out of the atmosphere. A critic, representing the vast majority of scientific opinion, rose to challenge these conclusions. The sheer weight of the fuel would overpower its propulsive force, he said. Yet, Kármán defended Oberth, saying hydrocarbon energy could indeed provide sufficient thrust for such a task. The Hungarian declared Oberth's theory valid, but felt the technology to support it did not yet exist. The size and weight of the rockets, the right propellant mixture, the application of heat-resistant materials, and multistage firing techniques all needed to be perfected. Kármán saw only one serious obstacle to space travel: the problem of carrying sufficient fuel capacity for takeoff *and* reentry. He reiterated his views on extraterrestrial flight during his 1927 visit to Japan.

Thus, despite prevailing opinion, which denounced such ideas as pure science fiction, Kármán "always waited for the opportunity to do some work on rockets," believing the technological means would ultimately catch up to the theoretical basis. During his first years at GALCIT, however, the teaching, wind tunnel experimentation, basic research, and industrial consultations left no time for this earlier enthusiasm.[3]

In 1935, opportunity knocked on his door in the person of Frank Malina. An outstanding aeronautics student, he started at Cal Tech in fall 1934 on a mechanical engineering scholarship. But in his first semester, he registered for graduate aeronautics courses, acquitted himself exceptionally well, and became a GALCIT assistant. For the master's thesis, he conducted wind tunnel experiments on propellers, but soon found his real interest gravitating toward rocketry. As a youngster, Malina had been captivated by Jules Verne's *From the Earth to the Moon;* in his last undergraduate year at Texas A&M, he wrote an English paper speculating on space travel. Malina's final conversion occurred in March 1935 at one of the weekly GALCIT seminars organized by Clark Millikan. The group heard a fascinating talk on rocket-powered aircraft by William Bollay, one of Kármán's graduate assistants. Bollay patterned the lecture after a paper published in December 1934 by Eugen Sänger of Vienna, which reported promising projectile experiments. During spring and summer 1935, Bollay undertook design and performance studies on the specially powered airplanes and in October addressed the Institute of Aeronautical Sciences in Los Angeles. His calculations led him to conclude that such aircraft were not practical for commercial aviation, but could achieve higher altitude and greater velocity than conventional vehicles. Meteorologists, experimental physicists, and military leaders all stood to benefit from the so-called rocket plane.

The publication of Bollay's remarks in the Pasadena *Post* catalyzed rocketry at Cal Tech. The awakening paralleled the establishment of two German rocket research institutes: Eugen Sänger's at Traven and the Walter Dornberger–Wernher von Braun collaboration at Peenemünde. Meanwhile, in May 1935, Robert Goddard (funded since 1930 by the Daniel Guggenheim Foundation and operating now at Roswell, New Mexico) launched the first liquid-fuel rocket to exceed the speed of sound. In the midst of these developments, two young men appeared at the Cal Tech campus after reading Bollay's article in the *Post.* John W. Parsons, a self-educated but able chemist of romantic leanings, and Edward S. Forman, a fine engine mechanic, presented themselves to the GALCIT faculty and staff. Both were devoted amateur rocketeers, specializing in powdered fuels. They came to the Guggenheim laboratory hoping to find resources and technical assistance in constructing liquid-propellant rocket motors. Bollay met them first but, too busy with other projects, referred them to Frank Malina, whom he knew had a keen interest in the subject. The three chatted briefly and decided to pool their efforts.[4]

After several more discussions, in February 1936 Malina jotted down informal plans for an exploratory program in sounding (upper atmosphere) rockets. During the same month Malina, Forman, and Parsons spent nights and weekends casting parts for proposed experiments. Late in March, they appeared in Theodore von Kármán's office to describe their plans. In a sense, they entered a court of last resort. Just days before, Malina had asked Clark Millikan for permission to write his Ph.D. thesis on sounding rocket flight performance and propulsion. Millikan did the prudent thing; he gently told the twenty-three-year-old to satisfy this urge by taking an engineering position with one of the local aircraft manufacturers. GALCIT had as yet undertaken no power plant research and, in any case, Millikan, like most reputable scientists, doubted the future of rocketry. As Kármán himself put it, "in desperation they appealed to . . . the legendary professor from Germany with a reputation for being interested in unconventional ideas."[5]

The Boss gave them a sympathetic hearing. None of them knew of his earlier interest, and even Frank Malina only learned of it "much later." These experiences may have predisposed him toward the project. But he also liked imagination in his students and appreciated the "earnestness and enthusiasm" they exhibited. Finally, their technical backgrounds led him to believe that Malina, Forman, and Parsons could achieve what they wanted to accomplish. They sketched their proposition: construct and then experiment with liquid and solid rockets and, ultimately, fire them twenty to fifty miles into space. Kármán liked the practicality of their goals. They avoided the visionary objectives of rocketeers, who often dreamed of flying to the moon. Instead, Malina and his friends concentrated on penetrating the edge of space, above the height of balloon flight. Here they hoped to obtain data on cosmic rays and weather. Before the delegation departed, they left the GALCIT director with a written proposal, on which he would base his decision.

Malina drafted the report knowing Kármán would not accept an undertaking based only on experimentation. Like all the great man's work, it had to have a sound theoretical grounding. The Texan hoped to base his rocket project on Goddard's work and on the calculations of Sänger. Unfortunately, the specifics of the New Mexico experiments were not available and Malina and his colleagues had failed to unravel Sänger's methods (which involved the ignition of gaseous oxygen and light fuel oil to achieve an exhaust velocity of 10,000 feet per second). After much wrangling, Forman and Parsons accepted Malina's premise that the engine must be perfected and tested *before* building the rocket shell, propellant reservoir, and launch system. At the same time, fundamental research on thermodynamic problems and flight characteristics would have to be undertaken. The two rocketeers preferred to begin model launches immediately, but grudgingly accepted the GALCIT practice of first understanding the physical principles involved, then testing them experimentally, and finally seeking financial support after some initial successes.

The papers placed in Kármán's hands in March 1935 reflected Malina's approach. The director held them a few days, then gave his student the verdict: proceed with the suggested plan. But he stipulated two conditions. He would fund none of their activities; whatever equipment they needed would have to be bought at scrap or purchased from the trio's own meager resources. Second, they could use the Guggenheim lab only during nonoperating hours. Otherwise, Kármán offered to provide advice, allowed Malina to write his dissertation on rocket performance, and let Parsons and Forman assist the Texan, despite their lack of official ties to Cal Tech. Robert Millikan gave moral support to the project, perhaps because of its applicability to his own cosmic ray research. So did

Professor Irving Krick, a GALCIT meteorologist who realized the value of atmospheric probes to weather prediction. But Malina knew the real thanks went to Theodore von Kármán who approved the nation's first university-affiliated rocket program and lent his prodigious prestige to an endeavor of doubtful scientific repute.[6]

In the early days, the GALCIT rocketeers needed every bit of available help, whether money, facilities, equipment, parts, or ideas. For the latter, they naturally pinned some hope on Robert Goddard, the great man of American rocketry. As luck had it, in August 1936, Goddard and his wife took a holiday in California. Harry Guggenheim, his main benefactor, pressed him to confer during the trip with Robert Millikan. The philanthropist hoped for close ties between the two physicists. A suspicious man, Goddard tried to avoid the meeting, but since Millikan sat on the Guggenheim committee that funded the Roswell enterprise, he had little choice. During the discussions in late August, the Cal Tech chief proposed a free exchange of data, full cooperation, and close collaboration between GALCIT and the New Mexico operation. Goddard appeared to accept the suggestion, but ultimately refused to comply with it. Despite growing rumors that he had become "possessive, secretive, [and] uncooperative," he could not bring himself to share discoveries unearthed over thirty years in the face of solitude and ridicule.

For decades, the rocket scientist had depended for survival on the largess of the Smithsonian Institution and the Guggenheim Fund. He endured countless cruel press clippings characterizing him as an eccentric and a dreamer. Over the years he had learned to rely on the patent office, rather than on open scholarly discourse, for survival.

Nonetheless, Frank Malina met him briefly at Cal Tech and decided to try persuasion on Goddard's home ground. Millikan forwarded a letter of introduction and in September 1936 Kármán's student stopped in Roswell on the way home to Texas. The trip only confirmed Millikan's impressions. While Dr. and Mrs. Goddard treated him cordially, the talks and tour yielded absolutely nothing of scientific value. He saw only the rocketeer's machine shops (in which were concealed all components), an empty launch site, and a tower. The two men talked before, during, and after lunch, but technical details never arose. Goddard resented sharp questions from a novice and suspected that Kármán had sent Malina merely "to get information" for his dissertation. On the other hand, the graduate student found his host exasperatingly uncooperative. Despite this unpleasant encounter, the senior rocketeer stunned Malina with a job offer. He may have abhorred cooperation with GALCIT, but Goddard certainly had a sharp eye for talent.

Malina could not help being intrigued, but realized this alliance would not work. He reported the frustrating affair to Kármán, telling him Goddard regarded rocketry as his "private preserve," and all who ventured onto it "intruders." The Boss reacted with disappointment. He knew Goddard had genius, but now realized his fatal limitation. "If he had taken others into his confidence," wrote Kármán, "I think he would have developed workable high-altitude rockets and his achievements would have been greater . . . But not listening to, or communicating with, other qualified people hindered his accomplishments." Malina had already learned the lesson in the weekly GALCIT seminars: "the trouble with secrecy," Kármán told students and colleagues, "is that one can easily go in the wrong direction and never know it."[7]

"We did our best," lamented Frank Malina, "to try and get some kind of cooperation with Goddard with absolutely no success." The fledgling rocket project thus embarked on its work without the help it might have had. During summer 1936 he and Parsons logged many long miles on the Los Angeles freeways looking for such simple items as pressure tanks, fittings, and meters for the initial engine experiments. Even sixty dollars for a used gauge seemed like a great deal of money. During October, the three young men found "an ideal location" in which to test their motor: a dry, uninhabited canyon called the Arroyo Seco, tucked behind Devil's Gate Dam, three miles above the Rose Bowl, in the foothills of the San Gabriel Mountains. At 9 A.M. on Saturday, October 31, a GALCIT truck rumbled up to the site and unloaded the makeshift equipment for the first engine firing. Four hours later, with two cameramen and William Bollay and his wife in attendance, Malina and his two friends started the machinery. Despite an incendiary oxygen hose, the gaseous oxygen-methylalcohol mixture performed well. The following January, the motor ran for 44 seconds under pressure of 75 pounds per square inch.[8]

Naturally, this news encouraged Kármán. But before he endorsed the project fully, he insisted upon theoretical substantiation for rocket flight; did fundamental laws of aerodynamics prevent projectiles from penetrating the earth's atmosphere? Without such findings, the motor tests were mere engineering curiosities. Malina realized by January 1937 that he must either demonstrate the scientific basis of practical rocketry or lose his mentor's support. Working with the brilliant Chinese doctoral candidate Hsue-Shen Tsien[9] on the thermodynamics of the motor and the equally talented master's student Apollo Milton Olin (Amo) Smith on a theory of sounding rocket dynamics, the team spent much of February and March embroiled in the problems. If the Boss liked the analyses, Malina would make a modest request: permanent space in the Guggenheim building.

The experience proved illuminating. Subjected to hard scientific scrutiny, the proposed rocket at first seemed to have far less potential thrust than anyone thought. By early March, Malina thought he should choose a new dissertation subject. But the following week he discovered an approximate solution that described a projectile attaining heights of several hundred thousand feet. Clark Millikan read and approved the analysis and handed it to Kármán at the end of the month. The GALCIT director made a preliminary review on April 10, but held back the analysis for a week to consider its merits carefully. On its strength he would either give the project its birth certificate, or terminate it. On April 16, 1937, Kármán made the decision. That afternoon, he invited Malina and William Bollay to Marengo Avenue to discuss the future of Cal Tech rocketry. They left in a state of euphoria. Malina felt vindicated.

> Now definitely I feel certain of Kármán's interest and therefore backing of the department, not sufficiently financially, but at least in every other way. The next two months I am to become a promoter, looking for a financial backer . . . A nice job and one for which I have not made a method of attack to follow. There are several leads to investigate, but nothing definite can be said about the success to be expected. Now that Kármán's blessing has been obtained, we are going ahead with renewed hope.[10]

Spring 1937 brought plenty of reason for hope. Kármán not only rewarded the group with important moral support, he now took the gamble of letting them occupy the basement of the GALCIT building. Here they would test potentially explosive propellants on small-scale motors. No longer would Malina, Forman, Parsons, Amo Smith, and Tsien have to drive to the Arroyo Seco, assemble test stands, and disassemble them upon completion. In fact, specialization of tasks began to occur. Parsons delved into the chemistry of propellants, Smith worked out laboratory plans, and Malina concentrated on fundraising.

The Texan's job became easier as a result of yet another benefit bestowed by Kármán. At the end of April he asked Malina to report to the GALCIT seminar on the rocket project's first year of operation. During the presentation, a young assistant from the Cal Tech Astrophysical Laboratory named Weld Arnold became so enthused that he offered to donate one thousand dollars to the cause, provided he could act as project photographer. Malina accepted with disbelief, and relief. At the end of May Arnold, the sixth member of the Cal Tech rocketeers, ended the group's destitution with a "downpayment" of one hundred dollars, stacked impressively in singles and five-dollar bills. Regular payments followed throughout the summer. As if to recognize their good fortune, the band of experimenters acquired an official name: the GALCIT Rocket Research Project. Toward the end of July the cellar of the Guggenheim building teemed with researchers and equipment; a bona fide laboratory had finally opened for business.[11]

Unfortunately, Kármán's gamble became Kármán's folly. Just a week after moving indoors, Malina and company tried a series of simple tests to measure the potency of various combinations of liquid propellants. They attached a fifty-foot pendulum to the ceiling of the third floor and suspended it down to the basement. The top end swung freely, the bottom was attached to a motor powered by a variety of oxidizer-liquid-fuel cocktails. When the engine turned over, it would push the end of the pendulum and the thrust achieved from each mixture would be plotted. But on the first attempt the motor misfired, sending a toxic and odorous cloud of $NO_2$-alcohol into all five floors of GALCIT. Because of oxidation, a thin coat of rust formed on almost every piece of machinery in the structure.

Kármán needed to act quickly. The incident only lowered the already tenuous reputation of rocketry among the Cal Tech community. Moreover, he knew Robert Millikan would not tolerate a threat to the health and safety of students and staff. Some of the GALCIT faculty grumbled about the dangers to which everyone had been exposed. Kármán's daring band even became the butt of humor; students branded them the Suicide Club. Amused but still concerned, the Boss stopped the indoor tests and directed Malina to move all rocket work outside, to a concrete apron attached to the east corner of the lab. Not to be caught unawares again, the GALCIT director scrutinized carefully the plans for the building's new exterior and approved two modifications: suspending beams from the roof line to support a fifty-foot pendulum, and mounting a stationary test stand on the cement platform.[12]

The balance of 1937 and early 1938 went more smoothly for Theodore von Kármán and the Suicide Club. Seminal work proceeded on the use of storable liquid oxidizers in propellant compounds. In solid fuels, Parsons and Forman experimented with a smokeless powder rocket engine similar to one designed by Goddard. At Kármán's suggestion, Malina and Amo Smith polished and expanded the rocket flight performance paper they had written in March 1937, and on January 25, 1938, presented it at a meeting of the Institute of Aeronautical Sciences in New York. In the aftermath, newspapers on both coasts printed sensational headlines predicting three-stage rockets flying to altitudes of 5 million feet at velocities of 11,000 miles per second. When the Los Angeles *Times* carried the story and the Associated News wire service published Malina's photograph, reporters appeared on the Cal Tech campus for the latest bulletins. Kármán issued a warning to the Suicide Club to hold down publicity until more tangible research results were obtained.

Such findings began to materialize, thanks to studies by Malina and Tsien, with assistance from the Boss. Just as he had worked with Amo Smith on flight dynamics, Malina assisted Tsien in developing the preliminary paper on rocket motor thermodynamics written in March 1937. During winter 1938 they struggled with the calculations and decided, upon completion, to test their theories by building a constant-volume solid-propellant engine. Not accidently, the first Malina-Tsien rocket motor experiment, undertaken early in May 1938, coincided with Kármán's approval of their theoretical work. Despite some excessive noise, two firings in May met with significant success.

Frank Malina now felt confident enough about the project to publish a short article detailing the technical and administrative workings of the GALCIT rocket operation. Inside the organization, however, signs of trouble became evident early in summer 1938. Amo Smith left Cal Tech for an engineering position at Douglas Aircraft. Weld Arnold dropped out of school and moved to New York, not to be heard from for twenty years. Hsue-Shen Tsien became engrossed in his dissertation. Forman and Parsons ran out of money and took jobs with Halifax Powder in the Mojave Desert. Even Malina's interest wavered as Kármán involved him in a soil erosion contract with the U.S. Department of Agriculture.[13]

The rocketeers needed another Arnold—another good angel—and found one, thanks to their leader. Some years earlier, Theodore von Kármán befriended an Army Air Corps brigadier general who was commander of the First Wing, General Headquarters Air Force, at nearby March Field, California. Kármán's connection with Gen. Henry H. Arnold stemmed from Robert Millikan. During World War I, Millikan led the Army Signal Corps's Science and Research Division, where he met the young airman, then assistant director of the Office of Military Aeronautics. When he reported to March Field in March 1935, Arnold made a point of visiting Cal Tech to see his wartime friend. Ever alert to the possibilities of broadening the contacts of his school, Millikan introduced him to Kármán and the GALCIT operation.

Two more different men than the director and the general can hardly be imagined. Big-framed and hearty, Arnold had no technical education and traced his lineage to prerevolutionary America. He rose through the ranks on the strength of dogged hard work and service as one of the nation's first military aviators. He contrasted sharply with the slender, soft-spoken, scholarly Hungarian. Yet Kármán liked Arnold from their first meeting. In him he found a man who understood the importance of science to military success and who had a certain "vision and judgement." Though flinty and demanding, "Hap" Arnold appreciated humor, and Kármán's earthy wit appealed to this side of his personality. Moreover, the GALCIT director felt at ease with military men. As an officer in World War I, he was accustomed to life in the service, to dealing with generals and admirals, and to the intricacies of the armed forces bureaucracy. He understood and admired those who flourished in such an environment. Finally, Arnold treated Kármán with a high degree of deference, something guaranteed to please. Much as the Boss liked informality, only a few colleagues—such as the Millikans—referred to him by any other name than "Dr. von Kármán."[14]

Arnold "came often" to Cal Tech in 1935 to observe wind tunnel operations, during which times Kármán had "very many talks with him." He tutored the general on aircraft stability and engine performance, subjects that especially piqued his curiosity. Before the California assignment ended in January 1936, Arnold visited GALCIT one last time, to attend meetings chaired by Kármán on airship aerodynamics. The sessions pertained to the recent disasters aboard the dirigibles *Macon* and *Akron*. When Hap Arnold left the region to become the assistant chief of the Army Air Corps in Washington, D.C., Kármán assumed their paths would cross rarely.

Two years later, however, world politics brought them back together. Portents of war had been spreading across Asia and Europe, suggesting a global crisis and the need to rearm. Remembering what he had seen at GALCIT, Arnold made a surprise visit early in May 1938. Kármán arrived home from a trip to the east on the eighth, and greeted his famous alumnus the following week. After brief reminiscences, the Boss showed the general two important sites: the rocket apparatus spread

Maurice and Helen von Kármán, pictured early in their marriage.

Theodore von Kármán, aged three or four years. His mathematical prodigy manifested itself at an early age.

A powerful father, Maurice von Kármán exerted a profound influence over his third son.

Kármán as an undergraduate at the Royal Joseph University, Budapest, around 1900.

A respectable Budapest family, mid-1890s. Surrounding the elder Kármáns are *(left to right):* Josephine, Feri, Elemer, Todor, and Miklos.

Formidable teacher and rival, Prof. Ludwig Prandtl of Göttingen University.

Kármán's first institutional success: the Aerodynamics Institute at the Aachen Technical University. Photographed in the 1920s.

The director of the Aachen Aerodynamics Institute poses with his staff, 1920s. Not shown: the many German aircraft manufacturers who supported the Institute's research.

L. H. Föppl, wie steht's mit der Rück-
fahrt nach G.? Oder fahren Sie direkt
nach Hahnenklee? Hoffe morgen oder
übermorgen eine Karte von Ihnen zu be-
kommen. Ihr
Kármán

Bitte, meine besten Empfehlungen an Ihre
w. Familie zu übermitteln
Ka

In the service of the Austro-Hungarian Empire. Lieutenant von Kármán, pictured around 1917.

A dashing figure of Aachen café society, late 1920s.

Adviser to the Kawanishi Company, 1927. Here Kármán adopts the shoeless habit of his guests.

After four years of courting, Cal Tech leader Robert A. Millikan and philanthropist Harry Guggenheim persuaded Kármán to direct the Guggenheim Aeronautical Laboratory at the California Institute of Technology. In the foreground, Irving Krick *(far left)*, Robert Millikan, Clark Millikan, and Kármán *(fourth, fifth, and sixth from left)*, and John W. Parsons *(far right)*.

The soul of GALCIT: the ten-foot wind tunnel and supporting staff. Clark Millikan *(fourth from left)* and Kármán *(sixth from left)* stand beneath the impressive structure.

At the door of GALCIT, joking *(left to right)* with Clark Millikan, Irving Krick, and Arthur Klein. About 1930.

A conversation in the desert with rocket scientist Eugen Sänger, 1933. Two years later, Sänger's theories sparked an interest in rocketry at GALCIT.

Josephine (Pipö) von Kármán, her brother's closest confidant, adviser, and friend, mid-1930s.

Kármán's fine house at 1501 South Marengo Avenue, Pasadena, a mecca for the American aeronautics community. The Boss held court here from 1930 to 1944. Although he later shifted his life to Washington, D.C. (1945 to 1950), and Paris (1951 to 1963), the home remained dear to him and he maintained it even though he lived there only a fraction of the year. (*Source:* Courtesy of the USAF Academy Library)

The Kármán living room, filled with Asiatic furnishings. During frequent parties, it was equally jammed with friends, colleagues, and students. (*Source:* Courtesy of the USAF Academy Library)

The dining room, where guests were treated to platters of food and drink brought forth from the adjoining kitchen by Helen and Josephine von Kármán. Note the presence of Maurice von Kármán on the wall to the right. (*Source:* Courtesy of the USAF Academy Library)

Kármán's study, scene of countless midnight conferences and aeronautical discoveries, large and small. (*Source:* Courtesy of the USAF Academy Library)

The world-famous Douglas Commercial (DC-)3 aircraft. Note the "Kármán Fillet," the streamlined surface over the juncture between the upper wing and fuselage. (*Source:* USAF photograph)

*From left:* Frank J. Malina, William F. Durand, and Kármán ponder the success of jet-assisted takeoff (JATO) before its first flight test in August 1941. The first JATOs used solid propellants.

Pipö, Kármán, and six Asian students. Kneeling, *at left,* is Hsue-Shen Tsien, brilliant theorist of rocketry and member of the Suicide Club.

Decked in headgear for protection against the summer heat of March Field, California, Kármán makes some final JATO calculations. Looking on *(left to right)* are Clark Millikan, Martin Summerfield, Frank J. Malina, and Army Air Forces pilot Homer Boushey.

JATO launched, August 16, 1941. The test vehicle, an Ercoupe aircraft, climbs steeply while a Porterfield airplane, which took off from the same position, still taxis on the ground. The success of JATO led to large military contracts and the founding of Aerojet Engineering. (*Source:* Courtesy of the USAF Academy Library)

The JATO rocketeers, March Field, August 1941. *Left to right:* Fred P. Miller, John W. Parsons, Edward S. Forman, Frank J. Malina, Capt. Homer Boushey, and two Army Air Corps mechanics stand in front of the Ercoupe. (*Source:* Courtesy of the USAF Academy Library)

Founding members of the Aerojet Engineering Corporation (except for Col. Paul H. Dane {*fourth from left*}, director of the Army Air Forces Jet Laboratory at Wright Field). Photographed in front of the Havoc Bomber are: Theodore C. Coleman (director of Aerojet), John W. Parsons (vice-president), Edward S. Forman (vice-president, Production), Andrew G. Haley (president), Kármán (founder and chairman of the board), Frank J. Malina (secretary-treasurer), Martin Summerfield (vice-president, Engineering), and T. Edward Beehan (general manager). (*Source:* Courtesy of the USAF Academy Library)

At the end of World War II, Kármán interviewed German scientists for Hap Arnold. Here, between bitter interrogations, Kármán (in major general's uniform, *second from right*) and Ludwig Prandtl *(second from left)* smile for a photographer. At either end are members of the Kármán mission, Dr. Hugh L. Dryden *(left)* and Dr. H. S. Tsien *(right)*.

Once the feasibility of solid propellant JATOs had been proven, the more volatile liquid fuel JATOs were tested on Muroc Dry Lake, California. Pictured here, a Havoc Attack Bomber (A-20B), piloted by Army Air Forces Col. Paul H. Dane, achieved a sharp angle of climb in flights on January 7 and 8, 1943. (*Source:* Courtesy of the USAF Academy Library)

One of the most important weapons of World War II was the V-2 long-range rocket, developed by the Peenemünde scientists, whom Kármán and his associates questioned in spring 1945. This V-2 is being placed in position for test firing in May 1946. (*Source:* USAF photograph)

Commanding General of the Army Air Forces Henry H. Arnold. Not a technically schooled man, Arnold grasped the importance of science to air power and felt Theodore von Kármán was the best man to bring the aeronautical arts to the Army Air Forces. (*Source:* USAF photograph)

Kármán in his Pentagon office, where he presided as chairman of the Scientific Advisory Board. Photograph taken around 1947. (*Source:* USAF photograph)

A group photograph of members of the Scientific Advisory Board, taken in the Pentagon at their first meeting on June 17, 1946. Seated *(left to right):* Dr. George E. Valley, Jr., Dr. Frank L. Wattendorf, Dr. George A. Morton, Dr. Nathan M. Newmark, Dr. Walter S. Hunger, Dr. Lee A. DuBridge, Dr. Detlev Bronk, Dr. Theodore von Kármán, Dr. Charles W. Bray, Dr. C. Richard Soderberg, Dr. Courtland D. Perkins, Dr. Charles S. Draper, Dr. Harold T. Friis, and Dr. William R. Sears. Standing *(left to right):* Dr. Pol E. Duwez, Dr. Hsue-Shen Tsien, Dr. William H. Pickering, Dr. Ivan A. Getting, Dr. W. J. Sweeney, Dr. W. Randolph Lovelace, II, Dr. Julius A. Stratton, Dr. Duncan P. MacDougall, Dr. Edward M. Purcell, Dr. Vladimir K. Zworykin, Dr. Fritz Zwicky, Mr. Robert H. Kent, Col. William S. Stone, and Col. Roscoe C. Wilson. Those members not present at the meeting are Prof. Enrico Fermi, Dr. George Gamow, Dr. Hugh L. Dryden, Dr. Walter A. MacNair, and Col. Benjamin C. Holzman. (*Source:* USAF photograph)

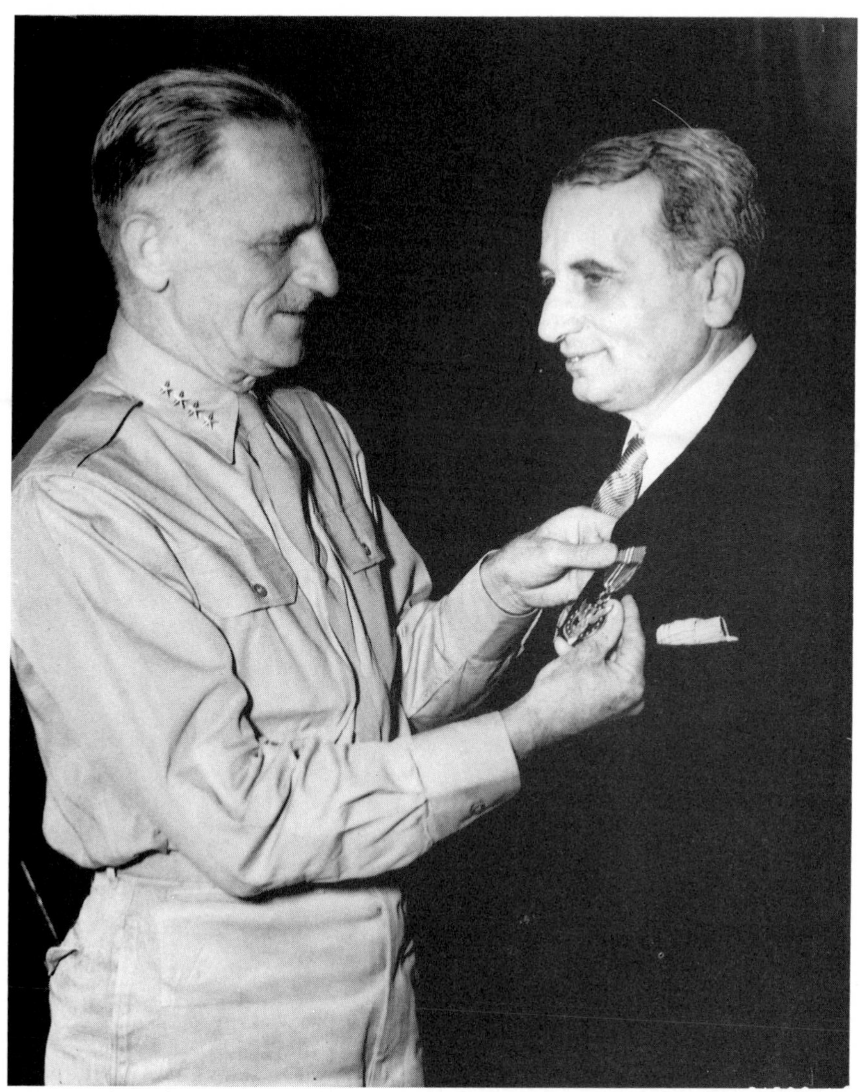

In honor of his labors on behalf of *Toward New Horizons*, in June 1946 Kármán received the Presidential Medal for Merit, the highest war time decoration for a civilian. Pinning the ribbon to his lapel is Gen. Carl A. Spaatz, successor to Hap Arnold. (*Source:* USAF photograph)

Brig. Gen. Donald Putt, former student of Kármán at GALCIT and now Air Staff Director of R&D, chairs a meeting with the Boss and Dr. Albert E. Lombard, chief of research in Putt's directorate. Kármán and Putt were instrumental in founding a separate Air Force organization for science and technology, the Air Research and Development Command. (*Source:* USAF photograph)

A happy celebration of his seventy-fifth birthday in May 1956 finds Kármán arm-in-arm with his companion of later years, the elegant Barbel Talbot. The former wife of an industrialist, she first attracted Kármán's attention during his career at the Aachen Institute.

Bow-tied and cigar in hand, Kármán strikes a jaunty pose in the Scientific Advisory Board conference room, 1949. (*Source:* USAF photograph)

The founder of the NATO Advisory Group for Aeronautical Research and Development shakes hands with Lt. Gen. Jean M. Piatte *(left)*, chairman of the NATO Standing Group. Donald Putt looks on approvingly during this mid-1950s session. (*Source:* USAF photograph)

Lt. Gen. Donald L. Putt, who demanded a sequel to *Toward New Horizons* and drafted Kármán for the job, much against the Hungarian's better judgment. (*Source:* USAF photograph)

Maj. Gen. Bernard A. Schriever, director of the Air Force Ballistic Missile program and formerly one of Putt's assistants, speaks as Kármán listens, around 1957. (*Source:* USAF photograph)

Kármán emphasizes a point to Schriever while Col. Charles H. Terhune, one of Schriever's assistants, looks on. (*Source:* USAF photograph)

The ambience of Woods Hole is clearly evident in this 1957 photo of one of the "sessions." Pictured *(left to right)* are B. J. Driscoll, an unknown participant, Theodore Walkowicz, Joseph Charyk, Col. Ralph Nunziato, General Putt, and the Boss. The man in the chaise lounge is also unidentified.

Kármán and Lieutenant General Schriever, now leader of the Air Research and Development Command, smile at a private joke, around 1959. (*Source:* USAF photograph)

At the dedication of the Theodore von Kármán Gas Dynamics Facility, Arnold Engineering Development Center, Tullahoma, Tennessee, October 1959. The Air Force defied its own traditions by naming an institution for a living person. At the ceremony, held in the Arnold Center's administration building, the portrait of Josephine and Theodore von Kármán, pictured here, was unveiled. Honoring Kármán were *(left to right)* Hugh Dryden, General Schriever, and Maj. Gen. Troup Miller, commander of the Center. (*Source:* USAF photograph)

Kármán in a familiar pose, engrossed in conversation with comrades, glass of wine in hand. Barbel Talbot stands at the far left.

The consummate partygoer beams approval of Mrs. Antonio Ferri's message while her husband, Professor Ferri, is distracted. Late 1950s.

Pres. John F. Kennedy awards Theodore von Kármán the first National Medal of Science at a White House ceremony, February 18, 1963. Smiling broadly with Kármán and Kennedy are Cal Tech president Lee A. DuBridge *(far left)*, Air Force Chief of Staff Gen. Curtis LeMay, and *(sixth from left)* Gen. Bernard Schriever. (*Source:* Courtesy of Vincent Finnigan)

An aging eminence wrapped in a robe, Kármán reclines in his living room, surrounded by mementos of a lifetime.

out beside the Guggenheim building, and the test range in the Arroyo Seco. They also reviewed some of the promising theoretical findings of Malina, Amo Smith, and Tsien.[15]

Neither Kármán nor Malina had thought through the military value of their work. But Arnold saw important warmaking roles for rocket propulsion and invited the scientists to visit Washington, D.C., in the fall. The Texan made no secret of his disenchantment with turning research into "better munitions," but could not resist the force of events. Local developments also pushed rocketry forward. Consolidated Aircraft of San Diego, one of the large regional aircraft firms, approached GALCIT with questions about the program. But rather than upper atmosphere exploration, Consolidated's president Reuben Fleet had in mind the more worldly idea of using rocket propulsion for flying boats. Probably the first airplane manufacturer to consider jet-assisted takeoff (JATO), Fleet raised Kármán's interest. Accordingly, Malina flew to San Diego and held a long conference with the president and his staff. He agreed to write a JATO feasibility report within ten days. For a one-hundred dollar fee (over and above the $7.50 air fare) Malina prepared "The Rocket Motor and Its Applications as an Auxiliary to the Power Plants of Conventional Aircraft," submitted on August 24, 1938. It concluded that rocket engines could indeed be adapted to boost aircraft to higher operating attitude and greater velocity.[16]

Encouraged by this rise in Suicide Club notoriety, Kármán awaited his next contact from General Arnold. Meantime, Harry Guggenheim brought Kármán, Clark Millikan, and Robert Goddard to his Long Island estate in a final attempt to form a cooperative arrangement. Representatives from NACA and the Armed Forces also attended the September talks. Like Arnold and Fleet, Goddard now believed a connection with GALCIT could be valuable. But Kármán's insistence on a totally free exchange of scientific data doomed the results. Even though everyone present pledged to pool information, Goddard never complied and Kármán finally voided the agreement. A second roadblock arose the following month when a high-ranking officer from the Ordnance Department told the GALCIT staff of the Army's poor success with rockets. He vowed not to pursue their further development. Even more serious, by this time the money contributed to the project by Weld Arnold had all but run out.[17]

Luckily, the *other* Arnold—now chief of the Army Air Corps—saved the day. Late in fall 1938 he asked the National Academy of Sciences to convene its Committee for Air Corps Research and review several pressing air power problems. The meeting occurred in an atmosphere of increasing international tensions; signatories to the Munich Conference agreed on September 29 to cede German-speaking portions of Czechoslovakia to the Third Reich. Impressed by the renewed importance of national defense, Theodore von Kármán and Robert Millikan, both academy members, attended the Washington, D.C., sessions. General Arnold asked the scientists to study two critical aspects of heavy bomber aircraft: wind-shield improvements and rocket-assisted takeoff. As everyone in the conference room knew, only Kármán's Suicide Club could do "the Buck Rogers job," as MIT's Jerome Hunsaker jokingly called JATO. Arnold asked the Boss to consider it and he agreed. Hunsaker and his associates accepted the visibility problem, no small assignment in the period before operational radar. The chairman of the academy's research committee, Dr. Max Mason, appointed Kármán to lead a subcommittee on propulsion, on which Clark Millikan would also serve. Kármán decided it should be called the *jet* propulsion group since much of the scientific community still viewed rocketry with deep skepticism. He also suggested Frank Malina direct the experiments, with the assistance of Jack Parsons and Ed Forman.

Ultimately, Arnold and Mason wished to learn whether JATO could improve bomber takeoff from rough fields, and if it added significantly to aircraft climb and altitude performance. First, however, they wanted to determine the project's basic worthiness. Kármán returned to Pasadena in early December and immediately searched out Frank Malina, who happened to be speaking at a Cal Tech luncheon on "Facts and Fancies of Rockets." He asked him to draft a report on JATO and be prepared to present it in Washington before the end of the month. Thus, Malina found himself with three weeks to write a paper that would either bless the rocket project with federal subsidies or condemn it to continued poverty and probable demise. He and the Boss completed the report on the twenty-first and Malina left for the east on Christmas Day. The Boss would meet him in Washington.

On the morning of December 28, at the Army-Navy building, the Cal Tech rocketeer spoke for an hour to an audience of scientists and military leaders on rocket motors, propellants, the existing state of "jet" propulsion, and a suggested program for JATO development. Kármán saw from the audience his student had won the case. Malina went home, but the Hungarian stayed on to negotiate the terms for initial JATO research. The Air Corps agreed to pay one thousand dollars to the National

Academy of Sciences, which, in turn, subcontracted with GALCIT for a formal proposal on jet-assisted takeoff. With this agreement, the Suicide Club was transformed; they ended 1938 as the ragtag, improvised Rocket Research Group and began 1939 as the Air Corps Jet Propulsion Research Project.[18]

After two months of winter inactivity, in spring 1939, Kármán told the rocket staff to speed up the timetable for obtaining test results for Hap Arnold. Air Corps leaders insisted upon seeing the first report by the first of June. The urgency stemmed from rumors of progress in the German rocket research program, as well as from Berlin's invasion of Czechoslovakia in March. Kármán could now accelerate research with cash. For the first time since the start of Cal Tech rocketry, he was in a position to pay regular salaries: forty hours a week each for Parsons and Forman, half-time for Malina. These arrangements helped step up the pace of work. But in the rush to meet the deadline, a dangerous accident took place. Toward the end of March the campus witnessed two loud blasts from the east side of the GALCIT lab. Students running to the site found Parsons and Forman dazed but unhurt. They noticed the force of the explosions had embedded a heavy chunk of metal deep into the side of the Guggenheim building. The flying debris slammed into the wall about three feet above an adjacent stool—parallel to Frank Malina's head, had he been reading test results in his regular seat. Luckily, Kármán had asked his assistant to drop off a typewriter at South Marengo, taking him away from the scene at the critical moment. The loss of Malina would have been a crushing blow to the project, as well as to the Boss.

As it turned out, Kármán only had to endure the wrath of Robert Millikan. When the Cal Tech leader learned of the endangerment, he angrily summoned the GALCIT director and threatened to throw him and the entire Suicide Club off the campus. He could not tolerate threats to the safety of the school or its students. Kármán offered a compromise: let the theoretical work and quieter experiments continue in the basement of the Guggenheim lab. Meantime, he and Malina would seek arrangements for a permanent home for rocketry in the Arroyo Seco. Millikan accepted the idea, but funding for outdoor equipment and structures would not be provided by the central administration. This left the Air Corps as the sole (and for the moment, unknowing) guarantor of new facilities for GALCIT Rocket Research Project Number 1, the latest name Frank Malina coined for the undertaking.[19]

Improvisation now became imperative to survival. Crude test stands rose on the west bank of the canyon, not far from the Suicide Club's 1936–37 endeavors. Meanwhile, in April, Kármán left for Washington with an audacious proposal for a complete JATO research complex. He asked the Academy–Air Corps Research Committee for a staggering $95,000 for building materials, shop tools, test equipment, general supplies, recording instruments, and salaries and hourly wages. The total did *not* include the cost of preparing the grounds and constructing the center. Despite a classic display of the Kármán charm and persuasion, the effort failed. Members of the committee felt they needed more detailed data before appropriating such an enormous budget. Kármán did persuade the panel to grant $10,000 "to carry out basic investigations within the framework" of a new agreement. During the last six months of 1939 the rocket research project would experiment with solid propellants to determine factors of safety, controlled burning, and thrust-to-weight ratios, and test fluid fuels to learn the properties of liquid oxidizers versus liquid oxygen, methods of supply, and proper cooling and insulation.[20]

Hard months of experimentation now lay ahead. To Malina, the technical problems looked "threateningly difficult." Nonetheless, the new grant bought additional support for salaries, as well as $6,000 for equipment, materials, and supplies. Kármán also increased his personal commitment to the project. More than ever, he coaxed Malina toward the fundamental physical underpinnings of the difficult engineering problems at hand. He also brought to bear the prodigious talents of organization and negotiation he evidenced in the earlier days of GALCIT. All the Boss's skills would be needed. Evidently, the Academy–Air Corps Research Committee still doubted the "Buck Rogers" project. Even Arnold's assistant, Maj. (later Gen.) Benjamin Chidlaw, asked Kármán incredulously, "do you honestly believe . . . the Air Corps should spend as much as $10,000 for such a thing as rockets?"[21]

During the last months of 1939, Kármán and Malina may have repeated the question to themselves. They first decided to let Parsons try solid fuels for JATO. But the go-ahead was followed by months of failure. Long, controlled burning, necessary for the safe use of rockets on aircraft, eluded them. All efforts to induce the black powder to ignite for more than a few seconds resulted in an excess of pressure in the rocket combustion chamber and in dangerous explosions. By December 1939, with the academy subcontract about to run out, Kármán and Malina knew they must either solve the riddle of the powder or lose JATO, and perhaps rocketry altogether. "Now we must show," Malina said, with a hint of hope, "that we are more clever than others have been." Despite the optimism, no breakthrough materialized. Fulfillment of the agreement had to be postponed until mid-1940, during which time the Cal Tech rocketeers had no more success unlocking the JATO secrets than in the earlier period. Top authorities on sky rockets and explosives were called in to examine the problem. All reported the same conclusion to Kármán: a powder rocket, because of inherent instability, could not burn for more than two or three seconds, a fact known for centuries. The test explosions continued. Yet, Kármán still felt an answer could be found.

After meeting the experts during the summer of 1940, the Hungarian asked Malina to drop by South Marengo one evening for a discussion of the dilemma. The two chatted for awhile, Kármán puffing on his cigar and enjoying a drink. Suddenly, he froze; the idea dawned on him. In the lab the next morning he presented Malina with four differential equations describing the operations of a restructured burning motor. He handed the papers to his student, saying, "Let us work out the implications of these equations: if they show that the process of a restricted burning powder rocket is unstable, we will give up; but if they show that the process is stable, then we will tell Parsons to keep trying." To his amazement, Malina found the pages held the answer to solid propellant rocketry. In theory, so long as the ratio of the throat of the exhaust nozzle remained constant to the burning area of the fuel, the powder would burn slowly and evenly. Over the following months, Parsons returned to the Arroyo Seco hundreds of times and used this formula as the basis for countless experiments. He finally achieved reliable results. The amateur chemist devised a paper-lined combustion cylinder in which he packed one-inch layers of powder, blended to his own specifications. To make the ingredients safe to store, he surrounded the powder with a shell of hardened tar, mixed in the molten state with aluminum perchlorate. The brilliant combination of Kármán's theory and Parson's chemistry resulted in the first proven controlled-explosion solid rocket motor.[22]

During the long quest to solve the quandary, the GALCIT Project No. 1 continued to receive modest federal support and to slowly expand operations. Thanks to Major Chidlaw, the Air Corps leadership decided to bypass the Academy of Sciences subcontracting apparatus and, as a sign of the importance it attached to Kármán's work, sponsor JATO directly. This did not mean the Boss and Malina enjoyed a trouble-free experience when they traveled to Washington in June 1940 to renew the 1939 contract. Like the academy committee, Hap Arnold and his associates wanted firm experimental results before fully funding the project. Also, tired from a heavy load of travel, conferences, and research, Kármán might not have been at his best during the presentations. In any event, the new one-year agreement trebled the previous one, allowing $29,000 for an ambitious program: continuation of the solid and liquid propellant tests, and aerodynamic studies linking assisted takeoff to aircraft performance and stability.[23]

The most important point won by Kármán in these negotiations was a permanent home for the Suicide Club. After almost five years of existence, the rocket research project at last had sufficient funds—about $16,000—to erect regular offices, shops, and test stands. The original plan called for a construction workforce of twenty-six men, chosen from the Works Progress Administration (WPA) labor pool. But after wrangling for months with the Los Angeles WPA office, Malina learned no help would be forthcoming. Relying instead on makeshift labor, construction began in August 1940 on six acres at the western side of the Arroyo Seco, leased by GALCIT for five years from the Pasadena Water Department. The operating portion of the rocket lab filled only a small area of the total site, leaving much open space between the blast and smoke of the project and the inhabited parts of the city. On a strip just 1,400 feet long and 200 feet wide, small, rough-hewn shacks rose in fall and winter 1940. Called (a bit grandly) the Experiment Station of the Air Corps Jet Propulsion Research Project, it housed a main building, a machine shop, and separate structures devoted to gaseous, liquid, and solid rocket propellants. Test pits for the three types of fuels were dug on the premises.[24]

With the breakthrough in solid propellants and the physical facilities finally in place, Kármán designated summer 1941 to mount prototype JATO canisters on actual aircraft for flight tests. At the end of July the Air Corps provided a low-wing, lightweight Ercoupe monoplane, which flew from Wright Field in Dayton, Ohio, to March Field in Riverside, California. Captain Homer Boushey, a steady-nerved pilot, GALCIT graduate student, and Air Corps liaison officer, agreed to fly the volatile experiments. Jack Parsons prepared several dozen canisters, each developing twenty-eight pounds of thrust over twelve seconds. Recent misfiring at the experiment station showed that, to ignite effectively, the units would have to be packed with propellant just before flight, raced to March Field from Pasadena, and loaded immediately into the Ercoupe's JATO racks.

During the first three weeks of August, Kármán and friends witnessed four progressively daring tests of the system. The first one, in which the small aircraft remained tethered to the ground, ended when a runaway nozzle punched a hole through the plane's tail. After repairs, Boushey tried again. He eased the aircraft to 3,000 feet on its own power and successfully ignited two JATOs attached to the underside of each wing. Then, on August 16, the pilot snapped on the JATO ignition switch as he taxied down the runway, adding the thrust of six canisters to the Ercoupe's own engine. Boushey catapulted off the March Field air strip like a slingshot, a large white plume of smoke trailing behind. "None of us," Kármán later remarked, "had ever seen a plane climb at such a steep angle." The extra burst of power cut in half the normal distance required for the aircraft to take flight, yet did not materially affect flying performance.

Finally, on August 23, Boushey again took the controls and, using only the force of twelve JATOs, brought the aircraft to an altitude of twenty feet. The tests, wrote a jubilant Frank Malina, "exceeded even our highest expectations."[25] They not only proved the value of rocket-assisted takeoff as an auxiliary to piston-engine propulsion. Even more important, they demonstrated the efficacy of slow-burning solid rocket propellants.

Success in the prototype JATO changed everything at GALCIT. Three months before, Malina spoke nervously of a $100,000 proposal to the Air Corps; one year later he would describe a $200,000 budget as a necessity. Undoubtedly, the national emergency spawned on December 7, 1941, by the Japanese assault on Pearl Harbor helped stiffen the staff's resolve. But the desire to capitalize on six arduous years of rocket research may have also played a part. Clearly, mass production of JATOs for the Air Corps would have to be undertaken by someone. In September 1941, Malina, Parsons, and Forman met with the Boss and suggested the four of them join together to exploit their hard work. Kármán reacted sympathetically, but felt their product lacked a proven technical record. After a little prodding, however, he joined them, and began to cast about for a sponsor. For weeks they debated the relative merits of three plans: leasing the rights to JATO to a manufacturer; building the units on their own; or simply acting as consulting engineers on someone else's assembly line. Kármán first tried to interest Robert Millikan in a partnership with Cal Tech. Millikan advised him to seek a different avenue; the school's charter committed it to nonprofit education and basic research, not private enterprise. Moreover, he gently reminded his Hungarian friend of the total lack of business experience among the rocket group. Hap Arnold also issued a friendly warning: the Air Corps wanted a sharp distinction between scholarly and commercial activity. He and other airmen felt they alone should decide which ideas to transmit to the nation's factories.

Undeterred, by winter 1941 Kármán had invested "a great deal of time" trying to retain a stake in the fruits of the rocket discoveries. He asked a number of corporate executives whether they wished to fabricate JATOs under a profit-sharing arrangement; that is, trade factory time for Kármán's knowledge. His friend Jack Northrop, first on the list, showed no interest at all, although he started his own business in a garage. Cliff Garrett, president of the Air Research Corporation, entertained the idea, but declined to negotiate seriously. Hughes Aircraft reacted much the same way. None of the firms could envision a commercial future in rocketry, mainly because their engineering staffs had no clear sense of its technical aspects or its utility.

The Suicide Club talked over this catalogue of rejection and, after favorable discussions with Col. (later Gen.) Franklin O. Carroll, chief of the Experimental Engineering Section at Wright Field, laid plans for their own company. During the last weeks of 1941 the four principles, joined by the Boss's attorney, Andrew G. Haley, and former doctoral student Martin Summerfield, met many times in the big living room at South Marengo. Haley, who practiced in Washington, D.C., earned Kármán's gratitude when he obtained a permanent visa for Pipö the year before. Now he provided legal and business advice to the rocketeers. Around New Year's Day, they agreed on a name for the enterprise—not Kármán's suggestion of Superpower (too much like Superman), but a formulation by Malina and Haley: the Aerojet Engineering Corporation. During January and February, last-minute jitters afflicted some of the partners. But in March the enterprise went forward. Haley contributed $2,500 and free legal services; each of the others found $1,500 to invest. With an initial treasury of $10,000, Aerojet incorporated on March 19, 1942, in Wilmington, Delaware.[26]

Naturally, a "branch" office opened in Pasadena. While the firm's test operations continued above the Rose Bowl until the end of the year, Aerojet established a storefront on the ground floor of the former Vita Juice fruit cannery on East Colorado Boulevard. Space requirements shortly sent them down the street to an unoccupied automobile showroom, located at 285 West Colorado Boulevard. The meetings held in these quarters were chaired by Aerojet's first president, Theodore von Kármán. The "dictator," as Malina laughingly called him, relied on the assistance of a board of directors, consisting of Frank Malina, treasurer; Andrew Haley, secretary; and three vice-presidents: Parsons, Forman, and Summerfield. In two initial acts of confidence, the board issued stock to itself and required all members to relinquish any personal rocket patents to the company.

Within two months, Kármán signed a pair of valuable contracts for the infant corporation. The Navy Bureau of Aeronautics asked Aerojet to develop solid-fuel JATOs with two-hundred-pound thrust and eight-second duration for carrier launches. Meanwhile, the Wright Field engineers placed an order for liquid-propellant JATOs of operational quality. During this period, the Boss and Malina devoted almost all their energies to establishing the company: recruiting qualified technical personnel, hiring assembly workers, and buying equipment. Their work increased after Andrew Haley was called to active military duty in Washington. To fill in, Parsons, Forman, and Summerfield reduced their hours at GALCIT and spent more time at the "plant." Even Clark Millikan, a little disappointed at being excluded from the Aerojet founding circle, actively participated after purchasing some of the firm's stock.

Actually, these men assumed more responsibility because Kármán could not. Just as the business geared up, the Army Air Forces (successor to the Army Air Corps) canceled the liquid JATO contract. Angry and disconcerted, the Boss and Malina hurried to Dayton to find out what happened. Benjamin Chidlaw, now a colonel and chief of the Wright Field Experimental Engineering Branch, explained. "We like you . . . Doctor, . . . only in cap and gown. The derby hat of the businessman doesn't befit you." In other words, the air power leadership reasserted its position that production contracts must be divorced from institutions of basic research. Scientists, they felt, best served the nation by doing science. To alleviate the impasse, the GALCIT director resigned the Aerojet presidency, whereupon his associates voted him chairman of the board. His obvious successor was Andrew Haley, a canny businessman. Yet Haley, now in uniform, appeared to be out of the running. Kármán needed help and made an early morning call to Hap Arnold. The chief of the Army Air Forces failed to see why his friend wanted the services of a lawyer rather than a physicist or engineer. But he granted Haley the discharge within hours.

Once Kármán's status had been clarified, Aerojet started to blossom. In July 1942 it won back the big Air Forces contract. Late in August the company installed its second president, who proved to be very able. Until then, the business had experienced growth without profit, typical of an enterprise with little capital. Indeed, the company owed a local bank $1,000 and Malina another $2,000. But in October Kármán, the "super salesman and diplomat," made some real inroads in Washington. Government advances for salaries began to pour in and by December 1942 the 150 Aerojet employees represented ten times the number on the payroll just three months before.[27]

At the holiday season, the Guggenheim lab always hosted a lively Christmas party. Santa Claus never failed to grace these happy affairs, and this year passed true to form. At the designated moment, to the delight of adults as well as children, out stepped a marvelous St. Nicholas—stocky, round-faced, animated, and genial. Every year Santa gave away his identify when he spoke. Out came the soft, deep Hungarian sentences and accented "Ho-Ho-Ho" 's. A Jack Daniel's, a cigar, and a wayward hand on an attractive female partygoer removed any doubt about the man beneath the white beard and red suit.

Joyful as the event may have been, in December 1942, there was a hint of sadness. "He cannot avoid the trips East," said Frank Malina, "as various agencies keep asking for his advice." Through rocketry, he had become well known to the U.S. Armed Forces for his indispensable aeronautical knowledge. Henceforth, Kármán's friends in Pasadena would see him less and less. His connection to Aerojet attenuated with Haley's succession. Clark Millikan all but directed the Guggenheim lab. Frank Malina ran GALCIT Project Number 1. Not that Kármán abdicated his role in these institutions—the Boss knew precisely what went on and the major decisions remained his. But until—and even beyond—the end of the Second World War, his main work centered on advising the military. Between 1935 and 1942, Theodore von Kármán became an American in sympathy and orientation. He profited financially, professionally, and personally from the new life. In the following years, he consciously strove to repay the debt to his adopted country, a responsibility he felt keenly and pursued with customary vigor.[28]

CHAPTER 6

# A Wartime Mission

Once America became embroiled in a war with Japan and Germany, Theodore von Kármán found himself in perpetual motion, traveling all points on the compass to practice the art of aeronautical troubleshooting. Meetings with men like Hap Arnold, Frank Carroll, and Ben Chidlaw crowded his calendar. So did conferences in the boardrooms of Northrop, Boeing, and Consolidated Aircraft. Accordingly, his life became less home-centered. Military and commercial aircraft ferried him from Los Angeles to Dayton to Washington, D.C., and back again to the West Coast.

But Marengo Avenue truly shrank in importance in June 1941, on the death of Helen von Kármán. Her passing struck Theodore with profound and protracted grief. Though he went about his life and work with normal passion—the Ercoupe tests began less than eight weeks after her funeral—friends knew the sixty-year-old scientist never fully recovered from the blow. She represented a precious link to family and the old country. Moreover, her grace, wit, and intelligence constituted the soul of the Kármán household. Confined finally to a wheelchair, she nonetheless continued to act as surrogate mother to her son's legion of friends, colleagues, and students. When she died, the Pasadena address ceased to be the happy and important place it had been. Luckily, Kármán's globe-trotting helped palliate the loss and his sister Josephine, a frequent companion on these trips, became even closer to him in the years to come.[1]

Before the Hungarian could devote himself completely to advising the generals and admirals, there remained some important business to settle. First, a burgeoning Aerojet required his attention. Under Haley's guidance it acquired its own test site in Azusa, fourteen miles east of Pasadena, and in June 1943 won two navy production contracts for liquid and solid JATOs totaling over $3 million. Kármán continued as board chairman and engineering consultant. But by late summer, a crisis developed. The demands of production and the pressure to pay several hundred salaries far outstripped the funds at hand. The Boss and his partners faced a hard fact: control of the company would have to be shared with a firm able to infuse vast quantities of capital into the organization. As senior partner holding a controlling interest, Kármán took the first step. He asked Andrew Haley to open negotiations with one of his Washington legal clients, William O'Neill, president of the General Tire and Rubber Company. Through Haley, Kármán offered to sell General Tire half the Aerojet shares for $224,000. Haley brought back a counteroffer of only $50,000, which left Kármán aghast. Everyone, he said, had "poured too much heart and soul" into the company for such a meager return. But the Navy, sensing greater efficiency and lower JATO cost in the new arrangement, pressed him to accept. With sadness, he instructed Haley to agree to $75,000, for which General Tire bought 50 percent of Aerojet. Henceforth, the Boss acted as a technical director and paid adviser to the corporation he founded, which eventually became among the one hundred largest industrial firms in America.[2]

The second important piece of unfinished business concerned the GALCIT rocket project. By mid-1943, Kármán and Malina presided over eighty-five employees, spread out over twenty acres in the foothills overlooking Pasadena. The liquid propellant section had at its disposal six test pits and three assembly shops; solid fuels occupied six processing laboratories, two test pits, three storage buildings, two assembly shops, and a powder magazine. Production activities took place in a stock room and in machine, welding, and carpentry shops. A separate building housed the staff engineers. Finally, chemistry, metallurgy and supersonic jet labs had been established. In short, JATO rendered GALCIT rocketry a considerable technical enterprise.

But in July 1943 all the rules changed. British intelligence reports transmitted to the Air Materiel Command's experimental engineering division in Dayton related German progress on very large military projectiles. Accounts claimed the devices could fly one hundred miles on reaction propulsion engines, presenting unthinkable consequences to Allied population centers. Kármán agreed to read and evaluate the highly classified data, although the testimony was based on the dubious statements of enemy prisoners of war. With Tsien's and Malina's assistance, he sent back some intriguing observations that elicited interest from the Wright Field research and development (R&D) leadership. The Army

Air Forces's well-liked liaison officer at Cal Tech, Col. W. H. Joiner, urged the three men to study the documents further and determine whether U.S. science could compete with this monster.

The Boss found time to write just a four-page summary of ballistic missile prospects, entitled "Memorandum on the Possibilities of Long-Range Rocket Projectiles," dated November 20, 1943. In it, he frankly admitted ranges such as those attributed to the German weapon could not be matched by existing U.S. propulsion devices. But he believed true jet engines utilizing atmospheric oxygen might be designed for the desired one-hundred-mile distance. Kármán proposed a three-phased approach to long-range missile development: analyze projectiles powered by solid propellants, like the kind in JATOs; undertake similar experiments with liquid fuels; and begin studies on the air-breathing motor. After comparative tests among the three, Kármán thought a 10,000-pound rocket could be launched a distance of seventy-five miles. Colonel Joiner sent Kármán's views to Dayton, where surprisingly little interest was generated. Army Air Forces planners found the Hungarian's assessment too indefinite and cautious. But Joiner gave a copy to fellow Cal Tech liaison officer Capt. R. B. Staver and he dispatched it to his superiors in the Army Rocket Ordnance Branch. The reviewers there grasped its long-term potential. Less than two months later, a letter arrived on the GALCIT director's desk proposing a one-year, $3-million contract for a project far more ambitious than Kármán ever imagined. Colonel G. W. Trickel, assistant to the chief of Army Ordnance, asked him to begin large-scale—not scale-model—rocket experiments "as expeditiously as possible."

Kármán accepted the offer with pleasure. It entailed an entire reorganization of GALCIT rocketry. Once completed, nine section chiefs and 275 employees reported to Frank Malina. This huge project, known as Ordnance, California Institute of Technology (ORDCIT), planned a liquid-fuel projectile with a thrust of 20,000 pounds, a burning duration of sixty seconds, and a range of thirty to forty miles. With new responsibilities, the rocket research project received a new name. Its title first appeared under Kármán's signature in the November 1943 "Possibilities" memorandum. The Jet Propulsion Laboratory (JPL) officially came into being on November 1, 1944.[3]

The heavy demands of the rocket program, Aerojet, public and private consultations, teaching, and research finally exacted a toll on Theodore von Kármán's health. Friends noticed signs of decline during the war years as the normally buoyant and youthful looking Boss lost vitality. In June 1944 he became ill and entered a private clinic in New York City, where he underwent "a very bad operation" for intestinal cancer. The surgery was performed by a famous—and pompous—German doctor, who boasted he had saved Kármán's life. But after recovering "satisfactorily," the patient suffered two hernias, which developed as a result of the procedure and delayed his release. This fact gave Kármán a chance to prick the doctor's ego. "If an aircraft mechanic were to make a weld of metal similar to the junction . . . made in my intestines," he told the astounded medical man, "he would have been fired." Unfortunately, the doctor missed the joke, and grimly reported to Pipö that her brother had suffered a postoperative mental lapse! Only boredom troubled Kármán's mind. Anxious to return to his projects, he languished almost the entire summer in a sanitarium overlooking the cool waters of Lake George, New York.[4]

The opportunity to return to work unfolded in an unusual manner. During Kármán's long convalescence, Hap Arnold spoke at length to Robert A. Millikan about the future of the Army Air Forces. The Cal Tech chief may have been surprised to learn just how prominently Theodore von Kármán figured in the future plans of military aviation. He asked Millikan to release the GALCIT director from his academic duties for an indefinite period, a proposal agreed to with reluctance. In the early days of September, Arnold placed a phone call to Lake George. He expressed concern to Kármán over his recent illness, and asked whether he was well enough to discuss an urgent matter. Without mentioning the subject, Arnold suggested they meet at La Guardia Field, one week hence. The general's calendar showed a change of planes at the New York air strip en route to the second Quebec Conference of World War II. Kármán was thankful to be recalled to action, and promised to be there.

They chose a beautiful day to discuss the future. A cloudless sky and fresh breeze presented a scene more like autumn than summer. When Kármán arrived at the air terminal, a military aide escorted him to a waiting vehicle and they drove to the far end of the runway, stopping next to a parked Air Forces staff car. The man inside motioned to his aide and chauffeur to leave, and welcomed Kármán in. From the first handshake, both could see the effects of the war on one another. Still the barrel-chested, open-faced presence, Hap Arnold looked tired. Kármán showed the expected weakness after major surgery and long recuperation. They spoke loudly to hear over the whine of engines and the winds buffeting the car. Arnold talked first.

> I am no {longer} interested in this war. We've won this war. Whether we've won by sheer force or superior equipment I don't know. But it's won, and I'm not interested. What I am interested in is what will be the shape of the air war, of air power, in five years, or ten, or sixty-five. You gather a group of practical scientists for all the new things. I want to know what the impact of jet propulsion is, of atomic energy, of electronics. Get a group and study that in the Pentagon, and make me a report.[5]

Kármán was dumbfounded. He had just started to feel well again and looked forward to Pasadena and all the activities underway in the west. Malina, Clark Millikan, and the others desperately needed help with many projects. The war seemed to be winding down, as Arnold said. If so, why should he go to Washington? But the general's proposal had taken him by such surprise, he could only manage a feeble objection: "I do not," said the Boss, "like to work in the Pentagon." After more discussion, he softened his position. "I can do this only under one condition; that nobody gives me orders—and I don't have to give orders to anybody else." Arnold reassured him, saying "as far as taking orders goes, I will be your only boss. Nobody will be between us. As far as giving orders is concerned, you won't have to do that. Just tell me what you want, and I will see that it happens." Without really thinking the prospect through, Kármán said yes. It afforded a new, more direct opportunity to serve the country. It also appealed to his adventurous nature. But, fundamentally, he knew and respected Hap Arnold, and he responded personally to his friend's appeal.[6]

Arnold, on the other hand, asked for the help of one of the nation's eminent scientists from motives of cool calculation. He himself had issued directives in June 1940 to wage the air war "on the continuous production of current types of airplanes." That is, radical advances took second place to incremental improvements. While victory in the air did ensue, German progress in jets and rocketry and the Japanese surprise attack on Pearl Harbor raised deep doubts in his mind about the wartime strategy. Henceforth, the U.S. Air Forces would have to seize all technological opportunities and seize them quickly, or face terror from the skies. To Arnold's credit, he had the vision to realize the technically cautious approach to air power in World War II would not further American security during peacetime. Future stability depended on a long and permanent lead in aeronautical science.

Kármán admired the intellectual insight implicit in this analysis. He had known it earlier. Before the war, Arnold attended NACA meetings regularly, pressing his fellow committee members to design aircraft with radically new characteristics, such as speeds of five hundred miles per hour. On these occasions and others, Arnold exhibited the capacity to inspire scientists to serve his ends. He sincerely believed air power would hold the balance in the life of nations, and men like Kármán respected his judgment. In this context, his proposal at La Guardia represented nothing less than an effort to find a new bureaucratic mechanism to harness civilian science toward national security objectives.

Choosing Kármán for the job was a stroke of brilliance. The Boss had worked with military institutions for thirty years and had mastered the ways of success. He had a special affinity for winning over the uniformed leaders, relying on a character of his own making, "the eccentric Hungarian genius." This much-liked, avuncular figure strongly resembled the real Kármán. In the role, he answered the officers' technical questions enigmatically, with puckish wit and off-color stories. The whole performance kept them a little off balance, allowing Kármán to speak candidly to the admirals and generals, to tell them when he thought they were wrong. In subtle ways, he put them in their place. Many times he arrived at the Cal Tech gates with high-ranking officers in his car. But, if a favorite security guard happened to be on duty, Kármán got out of the vehicle and enjoyed a leisurely chat, regardless of the passengers.[7]

All these techniques were put to good use just after he and Arnold parted at La Guardia. Fresh prospects rejuvenated Kármán, and he checked out of the sanitarium the week after the meeting. He then contacted Robert Millikan and arranged a leave of absence starting with the fall 1944 semester. For the foreseeable future he would make his headquarters in Washington, D.C., although he retained the cherished Pasadena residence and continued to live there about a third of the year. While he also asked Frank Malina to assume more substantive control of JPL, Kármán nonetheless retained close ties to Cal Tech as a lecturer and researcher.

Meanwhile, the new tasks awaited his attention. Kármán visited Arnold in his Pentagon office on October 12, 1944, and spent most of the rest of the month in Florida at the Eglin Field Proving Ground. Relaxing by the warm Gulf waters, he and three trusted colleagues—Hugh Dryden, Frank Wattendorf, and Dr. Vladimir Zworykin of the Massachusetts Institute of Technology—laid a structure and drafted names for General Arnold's board of aeronautical scientists. When they returned to Washington, Kármán's initial appointment as Army Air Forces consultant on scientific matters had been issued, effective October 23.[8]

The Cal Tech professor's induction into Pentagon life was relatively fast and painless. After all, he had some experience launching new institutions. Kármán quickly learned his way around the mammoth building, where he spent several "very busy" weeks conferring with military and civilian leaders of principal importance to the scientific panel. When not shuffling down the endless concrete corridors, he interviewed in person, over the phone, and through the mail dozens of potential appointees to the board. Dryden, Wattendorf, Zworykin, and George S. Schairer (a distinguished aeronautical engineer with Boeing Aircraft Company), served as his inner circle, assisting Kármán in contacting and nominating the most distinguished candidates in the nation. Toward this end, they enjoyed perfect timing. Most of the first-class technical people who worked in wartime research had not yet secured peacetime positions and were available for the venture. Thus, among the list of finalists, almost all agreed to join. Kármán's eminence and the board's high visibility also contributed to its popularity among those called to serve.

General Arnold lost no time supplying Kármán with administrative assistance. The staff included captains Theodore F. Walkowicz and Chester N. Hasert, two of the Hungarian's students in his course on jet propulsion; Col. Frederic T. Glantzberg, the group's military director and an MIT graduate; and Lt. Col. Godfrey T. McHugh, the executive officer. True to his word, Arnold did not hesitate to give orders in support of Kármán's mission. No sooner had the scientist appeared in the Pentagon than senior military officers offered him competing positions to the one tendered by Arnold. General Oliver Echols, the headquarters Army Air Forces Deputy for Materiel, brandished offices and assistants; Gen. Frank Carroll, now chief of research and development at Wright Field, invited him to work in Dayton. The chief of the Air Forces answered both men with customary clarity; Kármán would stay in Washington and work only for him.[9]

In fact, the general and the Boss had already established a fine working relationship. Their meetings had a common refrain: Arnold pressed for aircraft with more speed and greater range, and Kármán reminded him that responsible scientists based their calculations on fundamental laws of nature, not wishes. On the other hand, the GALCIT director often found himself *raising* the expectations of some general officers, who too easily dismissed as impossible some scientifically valid ideas. Based upon these headquarters discussions, Arnold presented his objectives on November 7 for the "Army Air Forces Long-Range Development Program." He sought a "well thought out" plan that provided a guide to internal programing, as well as a basis for funding requests to Congress.

To place postwar air power R&D on a "sound and continuing basis," Arnold asked Kármán to consider a few likely factors of postwar life. America, now a predominant world power, would continue to face enemies capable of threatening the security of the nation and undertaking major wars. But Americans would neither support large peacetime armies nor massive battlefield casualties. Even though prewar R&D had "often been inferior to our enemies," Congress might still slash peacetime Air Forces R&D programs, pinning false hopes on World War II stockpiles.

Given these possible impediments to an adequate defense, Arnold enlisted Kármán to search the far horizons of scientific discovery for ways to provide for the nation's aerial safety.

> I am asking you and your associates to divorce yourselves from the present war, in order to investigate all the possibilities and desirabilities for post war and future war development as respects the [Army Air Forces]. Upon completion of your studies, please give me a report or guide for recommended future [Army Air Forces] research and development programs. May I ask that your final report also include recommendations to the following questions: What assistance should we give or ask from our educational and commercial scientific organizations during peacetime? Is the time approaching when all our scientists and their organizations must give a small portion of their time and resources to assist in avoiding future national peril and winning the next war? What proportion of available money should be allocated to research and development?[10]

General Arnold made his intentions official on November 10, 1944, establishing Kármán's board of scientific advisers in the Pentagon. Lieutenant General Barney M. Giles, deputy commander of the Army Air Forces, followed the announcement by asking all headquarters personnel to act with "full cooperation and expeditious action" in helping the new organization achieve its objectives.[11]

On this basis, Kármán set about his job. First, the transplanted Pasadenan avoided possible conflicts of interest by terminating all consulting ties to Northrop Aircraft, General Electric, and Aerojet Engineering. Meantime, Hsue-Shen Tsien, by late November drawn fully into Kármán's Washington project, drafted a working outline of the long-range report for Arnold, entitled "Future Trends of Development of Military Aircraft." It included the categories of high-speed aerodynamics, means of propulsion, and methods of control.

By the start of December the Boss had not only decided on an organizational structure for the board, but staffed it. The four-room Pentagon suite housed a chairman (Kármán), deputy chairman (Dryden), and technical adviser (Morton P. Alperin), as well as an administrative aide (Lieutenant Colonel McHugh). The full-time members included Colonel Glantzberg for strategy and tactics; Frank Wattendorf for gas, turbo, and jet propulsion; George Schairer for aircraft; Dr. Louis Alvarez for radar; Dr. E. J. Zand for controls; and Dr. Tsien for rocket motors. Outside the nation's capital, Kármán selected twenty-two distinguished scholars to serve as paid consultants, on call for Washington meetings with the regulars. Five military officers with technical backgrounds, including Ted Walkowicz, rounded off the list. At the same time that it assumed a coherent form, the latest "Kármán Circus" also received a name: the Army Air Forces Scientific Advisory Group.[12]

Thus, in just two months, Kármán had erected yet another aeronautical institution. Early in December he rewarded himself by taking a short holiday in California, the first visit since assuming his new duties. Once again, South Marengo pulsed with activity. The Boss met with Frank Malina, whom he persuaded to assume the responsibilities of acting director of the Jet Propulsion Laboratory. Clark Millikan would retain overall supervision both of JPL and the Guggenheim lab. In addition, Kármán's friends at Aerojet and Northrop were informed of the severe restrictions now imposed on his consulting activities. He presented his students with the sad likelihood of his continued long absences from campus, for as many as eight months at a time. Those unable to wait would need to find alternate mentors and research projects. Just before Christmas, after about two weeks of such bittersweet discussions, Kármán returned to Washington aboard a B-17 bomber sent west to retrieve him.

Nine days into 1945, the full Scientific Advisory Group convened to hear Hap Arnold explain their mission. The Pentagon conference room held about three dozen people, the bulk of whom were worldly, mature men. Even they must have been jolted by the immensity of Arnold's assignment. He asked them to search every corner of scientific inquiry to find developments that might give U.S. air power an invincible advantage. They must look twenty years into the future and "forget the past; regard the equipment now available only as the basis for [your] boldest predictions." The general recited a long list of potential avenues of research gleaned from his talks with Kármán and his long association with NACA: pilot-less aircraft, supersonic flight, bombs of far greater explosive power, air interceptors, aerial reconnaissance, air-to-ground communication, weather prediction, and atomic energy. He encouraged his listeners to travel anywhere necessary to uncover wartime technical secrets, whether hidden in the laboratories of allies or enemies.[13]

As usual, Arnold left his audience eager to fulfill his ambitions. Starting in early February and continuing through spring, Kármán reconvened the group at monthly intervals to discuss the organizational and scientific questions posed by the general. To facilitate communication among the advisory group's far-flung members, the chairman assigned them to five provisional committees: aircraft fuels, radar, explosives, ballistics, and solid rocket fuels. The sessions among these specialists were designed by Kármán "to secure scientific insight in a standing Air Force . . . to secure the interest of the scientists of the nation to help the future Air Force . . . and to educate the people of the nation that for [U.S.] security we must have a strong Air Force." In monthly progress reports to Arnold and in personal memoranda, the chairman set forth the group's preliminary ideas. One such recommendation concerned every person involved with air power research, namely, the fate of government-subsidized academic laboratories established between 1941 and 1945. Kármán urged his boss to safeguard basic research by funding in peacetime those labs founded at universities during the war. Should the Air Forces agree to continue subsidies for these valuable institutions, Kármán told Arnold to leave them in the hands of civilians, clearly more capable "than military or regular government personnel" in solving technical problems related to military requirements.[14]

Such candid advice suggested the ultimate quality of the advisory group's work. To further its usefulness, Kármán and Arnold decided a scientific delegation should go abroad immediately, collect aeronautical data, interview foreign scientists, and integrate the findings with American experience. The group's heavy schedule early in 1945 reflected preparations for this tour. Even though war still raged over half the European continent, the chairman asked Frank Wattendorf to draft a list of prospective foreign sites. It proved to be a monumental itinerary. Kármán's former pupil proposed eleven countries, beginning with the United Kingdom, whose facilities were the best among the unoccupied nations. The laboratories at Teddington, Farnborough, and Woolwich—as well as some leading industrial plants—held insights on jet propulsion, guided missiles, radar, television controls, materials, and explosives.

Moving on to France and then the rest of the Continent, the mission would first view the aeronautical work at Issy-les-Moulineux, the very place where Kármán fell in love with aviation forty years earlier. Belgium had in prospect the Aeronautical Research Laboratory in Brussels, in addition to the V-1 and V-2 coastal launch emplacements. The tour of Holland centered on the Phillips Corporation, engaged heavily in advanced radar research. In western Germany, Kármán hoped to return to his beloved Aachen and journey to the aeronautical centers in Metz and Strasbourg. Neutral Sweden shielded German air power research from Allied reprisal, as did Switzerland, where the Zurich Institute under German professor Jacob Ackeret specialized in high-speed wind tunnels and jet engine studies. Finland and Poland were also unwilling hosts of institutes operated by the Third Reich. In Rome, the group wanted to observe one of Ackeret's faster-than-sound wind tunnels and interview the able Italian staff. Finally, Wattendorf urged Kármán to view Russian developments at Moscow's Central Aero-Hydrodynamic Institute, hoping for reciprocation after the many Russian scientific missions to the United States.

Getting to Europe proved even harder than planning the trip. General Arnold's staff sent a request for the advisory group tour to Army Chief of Staff Gen. George C. Marshall. Kármán and his top assistants—Colonel Glantzberg, Lieutenant Colonel McHugh, George Schairer, and doctors Dryden, Zworykin, Tsien, Wattendorf, and Lee A. DuBridge—asked to embark in February 1945 on a sixty-day trip. But the Wehrmacht's desperate December offensive in the Ardennes Forest delayed the go-ahead. General Marshall had already suspended all European travel by War Department civilians. Moreover, State Department officials warned of Soviet resistance to granting visas and of possible preemption of the Kármán party by the mission of Brig. Gen. John R. Deane to gather Russian scientific data. A decision was postponed until February 1945.[15]

In a sense, the delay proved salutary, giving the Boss and his colleagues an opportunity to define their objectives more fully. When they submitted a second travel request, they asked Marshall for unrestricted access to all scientists and industrialists involved in European aeronautics. Kármán wanted to interrogate the captured Germans and inspect their laboratory facilities, collect information on R&D activities in Allied and neutral countries, and confer with military officers in the headquarters of the European and Mediterranean theaters of operations. By this time, informal promises had been received from the Soviet ambassador to admit Kármán to the Union of Soviet Socialist Republics (USSR). The group requested permission to depart on April 15.[16]

Once German resistance had been broken in the Battle of the Bulge, the Army chief of staff saw no reason to postpone the Kármán mission. His approval actuated the bureaucratic machinery and security clearances, passports, and visas materialized in short order. The Deane group and U.S. ambassador Averill Harriman in Moscow expedited the Russian leg of the tour. A new itinerary allotted forty-four days for visits to London, Stockholm, Leningrad, Rome, Bern, the Western Front, and Paris. The scientists were issued temporary military ranks and uniforms to hasten their travels and assure suitable accommodations. Finally, a letter introducing the Hungarian asked those assisting him "take any steps necessary to see that the . . . mission is facilitated and that he is shown every courtesy."

Before their departure, Hap Arnold made clear the objectives of the Kármán group to Gen. Carl A. Spaatz, commanding general of the U.S. Strategic Air Forces in Europe. Since the panel reported directly to the commanding general of the Air Forces, they must be allowed direct access to the sources: *face-to-face* interviews with all technical people, *on-site* inspections of German facilities in the zones of occupation, and *full discussions* with the principal European military and technical elite. He ordered Spaatz to provide air transit for the scientists, facilitate full freedom of movement, make appropriate contacts, and in general give them his personal attention.[17]

Theodore von Kármán approached his daunting task with customary enthusiasm. Bearing the simulated rank of major general (and the uniform to go with it), he led his colleagues aboard a C-54 transport at Gravelly Point, Virginia, flew via Newfoundland and the Azores, and arrived in London on April 28, 1945. Here they encountered their first obstacle. Another U.S. scientific team, known as the Alsos mission, had already decamped from the British capital to the Continent. Authorized by Gen. Leslie R. Groves of Manhattan Project fame, this mixed military and civilian group was instructed to advance to German research centers and gather data on the extent and content of the Third Reich's nuclear weapons program. After some initial confusion about the roles of the two parties, Kármán negotiated a compromise with Alsos leader Lt. Col. Boris Pash: they would help one another achieve their separate objectives, exchanging information and personnel to the extent possible. Despite cooperation, the identity of Kármán and company would remain distinct. They traveled in Europe under the code name "Operation Lusty," which Kármán found "unlikely but pleasant."

After a few days in the United Kingdom, on May 1 the advisory group contingent arrived in Paris. Since the war now was reaching a climax on German soil, the itinerary had to be adapted to battlefield circumstances. While awaiting orders, Kármán received an urgent message describing a secret scientific institute located by U.S. soldiers near the village of Volkenrode, in a deeply wooded forest outside Braunschweig, northern Germany. The group sped through Strategic Air Forces headquarters on May 4 and pressed ahead to the hitherto unknown site. American troops had already ransacked the laboratories, but even the ruins impressed Arnold's science advisers. Founded and directed by Kármán's former assistant Adolph Baumker, the facility's fifty buildings had been disguised as farmhouses and camouflaged by trees. Baumker and his staff of one thousand concentrated on ballistics, aerodynamics, and jet propulsion experiments.

Kármán recorded the recollections of the Braunschweig scientists "who had not the time or inclination to flee." They talked freely about jet propulsion and guided missiles and supplied abundant data. He also led a painstaking search for documentary evidence scattered over the premises and hidden in the countryside. He finally unearthed most of the projects studied at the clandestine location and arrived at a frightening conclusion. Had the Nazi regime further developed its aeronautical discoveries and better organized scientific research, they might have prolonged or won the air war. While the government lavished money on its R&D establishment, it failed to cement close ties between operations and research. Most German military men regarded scientists as hopeless dreamers who must not meddle in the real business of war.[18]

In a high state of excitement, the advisory group chairman cabled Arnold and described the vast treasure of materials uncovered in Volkenrode. Some 3,000,000 documents—about 1,500 tons in bulk—would eventually be air-freighted to the United States to form the nucleus of the Armed Services Technical Information Center. Meanwhile, priceless reports on boundary layer control, three-dimensional wing theory, vibrations and flutter, rotating wings, armament, and gunsights poured out of Braunschweig and into Army Air Forces microfilm facilities in London. Indeed, Boeing Aircraft learned of the swept-back wing design and its supersonic potential from the Braunschweig cache, resulting in the famous B-47 bomber.

Once Kármán erected a system to harvest the riches of Volkenrode, he and a few others journeyed by C-47 transport to Aachen. To his horror, the city, whose aeronautical institute he had built from obscurity, now lay in ruins. All signs had vanished from the streets. The Technical University sustained only partial damage, but British forces had senselessly destroyed Kármán's old wind tunnel. A visit to Vaals found his home of fifteen years boarded up, but standing much as before. At Göttingen University Kármán discovered his mentor and rival Ludwig Prandtl still presiding over aeronautical science. The Allies had spared the institute in order to capture it intact. Meetings between the two men were strained and "especially emotional." The Hungarian demanded to know how a person of Prandtl's brilliance could retain loyalty to the Nazi regime. Under pressure, the old man denied knowledge of the death camps, or of slave labor works such as Nordhausen. This made Kármán angrier still. Then, to his amazement, Prandtl asked who in the United States would fund his future research. "I couldn't tell," the Boss later recalled, "whether [he was] horribly naive, stupid, or malicious. I prefer to think it was naiveté." Despite his distaste, Kármán questioned him not only about experiments in such fields as nuclear propulsion but about his collaboration with the regime in Berlin.

Meanwhile, Wattendorf and Dryden rode south to Munich, where they met some four hundred engineers and technicians evacuated from the Baltic Sea rocket works at Peenemünde. Kármán's representatives learned much about the V-1 buzz bomb and the V-2 long-range rocket from the institute's two leaders, Dr. Wernher von Braun and Gen. Walter Dornberger. Once the Aachen and Göttingen interviews had been completed, Kármán flew to London to hear briefings by Royal Air Force officials on British progress in jet propulsion and missiles. The mission then headed for Switzerland for additional fact-finding and returned to Paris in early June.[19]

While several more weeks of hard travel lay ahead for Kármán, his younger colleagues began to complete their work. Tsien, Dryden, and Wattendorf prepared to leave for Washington in mid-June, but first made arrangements to ship a great aeronautical prize to the United States: an unused Swiss wind tunnel destined originally for Germany. Despite the priority for transporting personnel, Dryden won "immediate action" for the dispatch of a B-17 bomber to haul this invaluable machine from a crate at Orly to a hangar at Wright Field. This and other large pieces of hardware, the frank and extensive interrogations of the European scientists, the pallets of documents and laboratory equipment, and the preparation of technical intelligence reports, all added luster to the Kármán group.[20]

The final leg of the odyssey took the Boss to the USSR. He received an invitation from the Soviet Academy of Sciences to attend its 220th anniversary and General Arnold urged him to "look around and let us know what you see." Ambassador Harriman secured the necessary clearances on June 19 and the Soviets dispatched a lend-lease DC-3 to fetch the famous scientist. A delegation of eminent French researchers shared the aircraft. Kármán found the Russian capital alive with victory. He was delighted to accept Premier Josef Stalin's invitation to share the Red Square reviewing stand for a gigantic military parade. He also traded toasts with the Russian elite at a sumptuous Kremlin banquet hosted by the Soviet Marshal himself. During the party, one official asked how the Allies should divide credit for victory over Germany. "Being a polite man," Kármán replied two-thirds to the USSR, one-third to Britain and America. "You are quite wrong," said the man. "Ninety percent to Russia." The Hungarian took the counter-offensive. How, he asked, should the British and Americans divide their ten percent? Three or four points for the United Kingdom? Six or seven for the United States?

Despite the feeling of elation arising from Soviet military triumph, the trip revealed more about the country's scientific organization than its aeronautical research program. Unlike Germany, scholars in the USSR received high salaries, many military honors, even superior food for their wartime contributions. Kármán noted approvingly the stars on the shoulders of their top scientists, as well as their direct ties to the highest uniformed authorities. He also praised the Soviet laboratory system, a "supreme scientific organization" that ranged from the Ural Mountains to the eastern Ukraine. Kármán toured experimental facilities in Moscow and Leningrad specializing in chemistry, propulsive power, semiconductors, and nucleonics. But aside from a visit to a cyclotron, his hosts prevented him from observing any equipment or facilities related to armed forces research. "This struck me as surprising," he later recalled, "since they were all in generals' uniforms." Worse still, he found it all but impossible to engage in the spontaneous dialogue with scholars and students which he relished. All contacts had been worked out in advance with ideologically correct scientists.[21]

Disappointed by these arrangements and clearly exhausted after two solid months of travel, early in July Kármán journeyed wearily but happily to Paris. He was not too tired, however, to try to cajole a beautiful Soviet intelligence agent to arrange a return flight via Budapest. She failed him, so he arrived at Moscow Airport in major-general's uniform, dragging along his luggage and asking every flight crew he encountered to take him to the Hungarian capital. One finally agreed and he arrived home, only to be met by colonels McHugh and Glantzberg who spirited him back to France. This adventure actually worked to his advantage. Hap Arnold arrived in St. Germaine just before the Boss reached Paris. The general, en route with President Truman to the Potsdam Conference, conferred with him on the bonanza of technical data yielded by the recent European mission. Arnold delighted in the news and asked Kármán to prepare interim findings on his experiences. The final report would be drafted at a later date.

Accordingly, the chairman and his staff returned to the Pentagon and struggled to record their impressions. Six weeks later, on August 22, 1945, he submitted to Arnold a seminal volume entitled *Where We Stand.* A summary of the existing state of aeronautical knowledge, it listed the "fundamental realities" of postwar air power, from which Kármán drew several astonishing conclusions:[22]

1. Aircraft would attain speeds far beyond the velocity of sound.
2. Unmanned aerial devices would hurl highly destructive payloads thousands of miles.
3. The detonation of small amounts of explosive materials would result in devastation over several square miles.
4. Interception of enemy aircraft would be accomplished by target-seeking missiles.
5. Only aircraft traveling at extreme speeds would penetrate territories protected by missile defenses.
6. All aircraft would be linked to a total ground-to-air communications network.

7. Independent of visibility and weather, pilots would receive data on targeting, takeoff, navigation, landing, and communications.
8. Airborne task forces refueled in flight would be capable of warmaking against the most remote targets.

Kármán based his predictions on the long strides taken in Germany in the fields of supersonic flight, missiles, and jet propulsion. Almost unlimited government appropriations provided aeronautical institutes with ample staffing, the best equipment, and the most advanced wind tunnels. Research in these centers suggested that stable flight at transonic speeds required both rapid acceleration and airframes with high lift-to-drag ratios. German scientists believed swept-back wings offered great aerodynamic promise for exceeding the speed of sound. To further these lines of inquiry in America, Kármán urged large public investment in immense supersonic wind tunnels, capable of testing full-scale aircraft models. "We cannot hope to secure air superiority in any future conflict," the Boss warned, "without entering the supersonic speed range."[23]

Kármán had also seen enough of Nazi-sponsored guided missile work to recognize its future significance. The Peenemünde group under von Braun had not only perfected the V-2 winged missile, but completed calculations for a transoceanic vehicle whose practicality rested on wind tunnel data, ballistic computations, and the V-2 experiences. Perhaps more important, in an organizational sense the Peenemünde community represented a total missile development program, bringing together experts in aerodynamics, structural design, electronics, servomechanics, gyroscopes, control devices, and propulsion. Kármán suggested the same approach to Arnold: open a well-funded, interdisciplinary institute for missile research. The Hungarian also foretold the unhappy marriage between nuclear explosives and the capacity to deliver them over long distances. He warned the resulting atomic weapons would revolutionize "future methods of aerial warfare [and] call for a reconsideration of all present plans."[24]

The advisory group chairman knew jet propulsion would likewise transform the face of air power. Many patents had been granted for jet designs before World War II, but their poor fuel economy retarded production. Between 1941 and 1945, however, factors of performance outweighed efficiency and jet development raced forward. During these years, new knowledge came to light on combustion in high-speed air flow, metallurgists discovered materials resistant to high temperatures, and engineers built turbine and compressor prototypes that far surpassed previous models. Additional research, wrote Kármán, would soon produce jet engines practical for military and civilian use, as well as more efficient reciprocating propulsion systems.[25]

Kármán recommended two other forms of aircraft motive power. For supersonic long-range flight, rocket motors—the familiar JATOs—offered excellent auxiliary propulsion. Second, atomic energy had vast potential. Once difficulties of reliable nuclear production were overcome, it would provide an inexhaustible power source, yielding 1.5 million times the volatility of gasoline. The Boss suggested the Air Forces erect a technical center to solve the main engineering problems inherent in harnessing the atom: converting the reaction to usable heat, transferring the by-product, and developing materials resistant to extremely high temperatures and corrosion. Once tamed, this source of fuel promised unlimited flying range and virtual command of the skies.[26]

Finally, radar, an indispensable aid to aerial combat in World War II, clearly had an even more important role in the future. Kármán urged the Army Air Forces to avoid complacency and apply "clever adaptation" of existing radar techniques. Rather than a "facility or attachment which will occasionally be used under bad conditions," he predicted its absolute primacy in flight, opening darkness and foul weather to regular operations. Its guiding hand would eventually govern bombing, gunfire, navigation, landing, and traffic control. Indeed, the chairman felt radar's influence would rival that of jet propulsion, and foresaw a time when air power planning, training, and organization would be adapted to its inevitable influence.[27]

In short, radar and such companion breakthroughs as jet propulsion, nuclear power, and missilery promised to transform the face of aeronautics. In enumerating these developments, Kármán's *Where We Stand* raised implicit but powerful questions about the uses of air power in the postwar world. The answers would call forth all of the Boss's powers of prediction, as well as his best bureaucratic finesse.

CHAPTER 7

# Advising the Generals

Having summed up the existing state of the aerial arts, Kármán found himself with the far more complex task of extrapolating into the future the existing body of scientific knowledge. This mission launched a long journey for the Hungarian. During the next decade the U.S. Air Force turned to him again and again for long-range scientific advice. The secret to his popularity lay in the success of the sequel to *Where We Stand.*

While *Where We Stand* offered an eye-opening synopsis of World War II aeronautics, Kármán knew much work remained before completing the full forecast requested by Arnold. In particular, he wanted to gather additional data on the German intercontinental rocket and to fill in the picture of supersonic flight. He decided to mount a second mission to Europe. Before leaving, he called together all the scientists for a late August meeting. The discussions centered on the long-range report and Kármán pressed them to establish its foundations quickly and begin writing. Pressures to complete it had begun to rise. The Japanese government announced its surrender on August 14, 1945, opening a new aeronautical vista for the Kármán mission to investigate. Even more urgent, War Department officials had talked lately of centralizing all defense-related research under civilian control. Kármán resisted strongly the logic of unified armed forces R&D. In his view, only those involved in the aviation sciences should control its resources. Hence, he spurred his group to finish the report and establish a clear blueprint for air power technology.

To hasten the process, Kármán persuaded his colleagues to abandon the earlier idea of producing an aerodynamics textbook. They also decided not to present their findings along the lines of classic scientific disciplines: physics, chemistry, mathematics, and so on. Instead, each participant would write a brief monograph relating his specialty to missiles, propulsion, radar, and other subjects of military interest. The Boss asked for completion by the end of 1945 and left Hugh Dryden in charge of the project during the second European sojourn.[1]

This time a smaller contingent accompanied him. He and Wattendorf, Tsien, Glantzberg, McHugh, and Lt. Col. Frank Williams of Wright Field embarked on September 23 on a C-54 transport called "The Sacred Cow." It had been one of President Franklin Roosevelt's official aircraft, now placed at the group's disposal by Hap Arnold. They traveled in style; Kármán and Godfrey McHugh played game after game of chess in a large living room suite while the others either slept on double-deck beds or ate meals prepared in a complete kitchen. After arriving in Wiesbaden, Germany, they fanned out to the United Kingdom, France, Holland, Switzerland, Sweden, and Italy. Three weeks later they would fly to Australia, India, and China. Despite the "delicate involvements" of entering Japan, Arnold asked Kármán to lead the mission there during the final two weeks of the tour and "observe, correlate, and draw deductions" from Japanese science. Kármán's old friendships at the Kawanishi Machinery Company would undoubtedly overcome some of the obstacles. As before, the group left with instructions to make first-hand inspections of research centers and exercise "imagination and scientific acuity in recognizing important scientific trends."[2]

The European leg of the trip proved the wisdom of making the first visit before the war ended. By now, nations and industries began to exercise the normal proprietary control over data and ideas, and the rewards became proportionally less useful. Members of the party also noticed that the Boss himself seemed less attentive to the business at hand and more alert to the pleasures of dining and socializing. The presence of Pipö may have contributed to these distractions. Nonetheless, late in September he held fruitful talks in Zurich with Professor Ackeret on laminar flow control. Here Kármán learned new methods of minimizing aerodynamic drag by pumping air through small surfaces on the upper and lower surfaces of the wings, thus "bleeding off" turbulence. He returned to Germany for additional interviews and discussed with British representatives the urgency of avoiding unseemly competition in luring German scientists to the Allied countries. Kármán also turned his mind to the introductory volume he agreed to write for the long-range science report. Despite many discussions with Godfrey McHugh, he agonized over the extent to which it ought to treat organizational problems: should he suggest a total restructuring of air power R&D or merely emphasize one or two critically deficient areas?

Events forced answers on him. In mid-October Hap Arnold suffered a massive heart attack. He phoned Kármán from his hospital room saying he would "greatly appreciate" completion of the science forecast before the end of the year. The general wanted to apply much of his remaining days in the Pentagon to reading and propagating Kármán's ideas. They agreed on a December 15 deadline. This hard fact, the expected loss of two weeks in travel, and a feeling of debility from the rigors of the project compelled Kármán to alter his schedule. "Much worried" now about finishing the report, the night he learned of Arnold's collapse he asked Glantzberg, McHugh, Tsien, and Wattendorf to visit Asia without him. Meanwhile, he would stay behind, "using the time for writing up my ideas conceived in recent months. I feel this is the best way to accomplish the job," he told Hap Arnold, and "am very anxious not to disappoint you."[3]

During November 1945, he checked into the comfortable Prince of Wales Hotel in Paris and did as promised. Working only with a secretary, Kármán found the necessary mental and physical resources for the job. He also availed himself of the fine scientific library at the Sorbonne, where in long-hand he wrote out the entire first volume, leaving blanks for the classified data. Actually, preparations went forward on both sides of the Atlantic at once. Kármán and Dryden communicated daily by cable and exchanged pieces of the introduction and the monographs almost as they flowed from the authors' pens. The Boss returned to Washington on November 28, to take the reins for the final drive. Two concerns remained: to produce a study on the "same [high] level" as *Where We Stand;* and to incorporate the findings of the Asian contingent, which arrived in the United States just as Kármán got home.[4]

A relentless pace drove the scientists to the deadline. Kármán warned the group on December 5 that they had just ten days left and vast amounts of work unfinished. A day or so before the due date, a finished draft finally materialized. The advisory group met to agree on final details and to give their creation a name. After some argument, Ted Walkowicz suggested *Toward New Horizons.* Not everyone in the group liked the title; did it mean all their wartime work had failed to broaden aeronautical horizons? The Boss cut off debate. Weary after a whole year in pursuit of Arnold's vision, he insisted they really had searched "the basic scientific potential which could change the future. The name remained." Kármán's opening book, entitled *Science, the Key to Air Supremacy,* arrived on Arnold's desk on December 15. The following thirty-two monographs, bound in eleven volumes, contained classified technical information and were distributed selectively to the headquarters Army Air Forces staff. The product of twenty-five eminent scientists, most headed for academia after government service, the report linked the far reaches of aeronautical knowledge to the future of U.S. air power.[5]

Kármán decided to answer the thorny question of R&D funding outside the rubric of *Toward New Horizons*. On an attached memorandum he presented Arnold a bold formula for peacetime research expenditures: each year, allocate to R&D 5 percent of the average *wartime* Army Air Forces budget. In the postwar world, this meant from one-fourth to one-third of total annual air power outlays. Kármán justified his expansive plan on national security grounds. The age of nuclear weapons demanded a powerful air arm for offensive and defensive purposes. To produce the needed bulwark, the chairman proposed a ten-year research effort leading toward supersonic flight, guided missiles, all-weather flying, perfected navigation and communications, remote-controlled fighter and bomber forces, and mass airlift of troops and equipment.

To maintain a focus on practical solutions to these objectives, Kármán recommended the establishment of development centers. Unlike laboratories, which tended to undertake abstract inquiries, such interdisciplinary organizations would contribute directly to R&D goals. A surge in spending for science and engineering also implied drastic changes in personnel, training, and institutional structures as the Air Forces became more technically oriented. Most important of all, Kármán urged Arnold to instill an open-mindedness toward potential scientific breakthroughs. "Problems never have final or universal solutions," he wrote, "and only a constant inquisitive attitude toward science and a ceaseless and swift adaptation to new developments can maintain the security of this nation."[6]

In *Science, the Key to Air Supremacy,* the Boss declared that warfare had reached a watershed in the twentieth century. No longer a drama of human endurance, it had become mainly a technological contest for control of the air. Aided by scientists as never before, military men must learn the future rested on the closest cooperation with the nation's laboratories and researchers. Kármán knew Nazism first-hand and warned of the fatal consequences of atomic power in the hands of terror states. Surprise attacks with nuclear weapons were not unthinkable, and he admitted the impotence of science to counteract them. Should only one such bomb penetrate a nation's air defenses, immense destruction would ensue. The answer, said the advisory group chairman, lay in a powerful aerial offense that deterred aggression by reaching remote targets quickly and with maximum impact; by attaining air superiority over any designated region of the world; and by transporting through the air large contingents of soldiers and materiel. Over its own territory, America must establish total control of the skies and erect a network of highly sophisticated warning and homing devices to detect incoming enemy forces. To achieve these objectives, "only an Air Force which fully exploits all the knowledge . . . science has available now and . . . in the future, will have a chance of accomplishing these tasks."[7]

Without organizational realignments these goals could not be realized. Kármán insisted science must permeate the Army Air Forces structure. "Scientific results," he observed, "cannot be used efficiently by soldiers who have no understanding of them, and scientists cannot produce results useful for warfare without an understanding of the operations." To facilitate the interaction, he asked for the direct issuance of air power research contracts to scientific institutions, exchanges of personnel among military and civilian laboratories, employment of paid technical consultants for defense projects, and establishment of university facilities for the study of military aeronautics. Kármán also sought to break down barriers between the Air Forces and the aircraft industry, both by drawing a clearer separation between R&D and procurement and by allowing firms to undertake large ventures and pilot programs at government-operated, applied research centers. Such places, combining complementary technologies, would concentrate on supersonic, pilotless, operational, and nuclear aircraft; conventional armament; and—on an integrated basis—aerodynamics, propulsion, control, and electronics.

The Boss also wanted to infuse science into military aviation by spreading technological education among the officer corps and attracting civilian scientists to the ranks. He envisioned a whole cadre of technical men in uniform, ranging from those with baccalaureates, to Reserve Officer Training Candidates with master's degrees, to a select 20 percent holding doctorates. At the same time, to recruit the nation's finest aeronautical scientists, Arnold and his advisers needed to seek exemptions from Civil Service pay schedules and work conditions. Finally, to advise on all of the questions posed in *Science, the Key to Air Supremacy,* Kármán urged the general to retain the Scientific Advisory Group on a permanent basis.[8]

*Toward New Horizons* did not appear in the corridors of the Pentagon without warning. Theodore von Kármán had far too much experience as a bureaucratic combatant to present his report without first preparing the way for its reception. Its ideas won the backing of many of the military leadership during informal discussions leading up to its publication. As early as November 1944, Kármán circulated an outline of subjects similar to those in *Toward New Horizons.* He appealed to Arnold in spring 1945 to give air power science control over its own funding, facilities, and staff. Indeed, almost as soon as German experimental facilities had been examined, advisory group members sent back reports describing the foreign labs as "more ambitious and forward looking than our own." They immediately asked the general to undertake the construction of a new development center with enormous wind tunnels. Hence, by airing ahead of time many of the concepts in *Toward New Horizons,* Kármán learned the headquarter's perspective on future R&D and readied internal opinion for the report's conclusions.[9]

Its findings met with wide approval. Hap Arnold declared himself "enormously pleased" with *Horizons* and predicted it would stand "for some time to come as a guide to the Commanding General of the AAF in discharging his responsibilities for research and development." After a careful review of *Toward New Horizons* by his staff, Lt. Gen. Nathan F. Twining, commander of the Air Materiel Command, wholly endorsed its recommendations and asked General Arnold to take "immediate action" to enact the ideas in *Science, the Key to Air Supremacy.* Air Staff Director of Research and Development Maj. Gen. Curtis E. LeMay seconded Twining's views. Even the Boss admitted mildly, "I cannot say that we did not see things." More important than any specific proposals, *Toward New Horizons* fostered an atmosphere favorable to basic air power research and established the concept of military aeronautics as a *national* resource, free from the exclusive control of civilian or uniformed leaders. "It must, Kármán said, "be dispersed among all the people and their institutions."[10]

*Toward New Horizons* quickly became woven into the institutional fabric of the Army Air Forces. Partly as a result of its publication and dissemination, planners at Wright Field and the Pentagon rebuffed the eminent physicist Dr. Vannevar Bush, who denied in public testimony the operational value of intercontinental ballistic missiles (ICBMs). They listened instead to Kármán's predictions of the ultimate success of ICBMs and budgeted scarce postwar resources for their development.

During 1946 the Consolidated-Vultee Aircraft Company won a contract to study such aspects of missilery as guidance, control, and lightweight structures. Meanwhile, North American Aviation undertook a review of guided missile propulsion. While these projects went forward, both the Air Materiel Command and Air Staff drafted plans to enact the Kármán recommendations. Much of their work yielded no results. Congress slashed 1947 R&D funding, appropriating just $111 million of the $186 million requested. The House and Senate persisted in austerity measures for the rest of the decade. Nonetheless, for many years Theodore von Kármán and his monumental reports exerted a powerful influence over American military aviation. He succeeded in persuading Air Forces leaders of the impermanence of technological leads and associated in their minds aeronautical science with national survival. His detailed, highly technical blueprint set the agenda of research and development for decades to come. Moreover, *Toward New Horizons* established a precedent of periodic, long-range science forecasting and, as the first such report, influenced profoundly all of the succeeding studies on aerial warfare.[11]

Despite the obvious value of the group's contributions, Kármán realized air power technology required a champion within the military establishment. General Arnold knew instinctively the importance of R&D to preeminence in the skies; his successors might not. The answer, suggested in *Science, the Key to Air Supremacy,* lay in perpetuating the advisory group itself. Less than a week after submitting *Toward New Horizons,* the chairman repeated to Arnold the necessity of establishing a permanent, peacetime body of the finest scientific advisers. Over time, he said, the value of unbiased, on-hand technical guidance would only increase. The nation's air arm needed "scientific consultants . . . familiar with the [Army Air Forces], but whose main activities are outside the [Army Air Forces]." Unlike the Materiel Command engineers or the planners in the Pentagon directorate of R&D, this new organization would concern itself only with "future trends and long range possibilities," not current research projects.[12]

The Hungarian wanted his board attached directly to the commanding general's office, consisting of a military director of brigadier rank, a full-time civilian scientist, a small staff, and ten to fifteen paid consultants "of a very high scientific standing." They would analyze problems and prepare reports on technical matters of concern to the top air power leaders. Arnold's faith in *Toward New Horizons* and reliance on

Kármán's advice attracted him to the idea, and he forwarded the request to Major General LeMay. Several days after Christmas 1945, Arnold received evidence supporting Kármán's claims. Lieutenant General John K. Cannon, Air Forces commanding general in Europe, sent him a letter asking for a man experienced in questioning enemy scientists. Many Germans were abandoning their homeland and Cannon wanted to make sure those with exceptional backgrounds settled in the United States. Cannon had a particular officer in mind: Col. Frank Williams, an advisory group veteran who had accompanied Kármán on his second European tour. The importance of an organization able to "speak the language of science" had become clear.

Discussions among the Boss, Arnold, Carl Spaatz, LeMay, and other high-ranking officers yielded agreement on a regular panel of scientists. Kármán's arguments won out, although General LeMay clearly wanted the new organization to be linked to his R&D directorate. But once overruled, he worked closely with the chairman to draft a framework for Arnold's advisory group. In their conception, the science board reported directly to—and received directives directly from—the commanding general, informed him of new scientific developments, presented him with special studies, evaluated long-range research plans, and advised on institutional aspects of military aeronautics. Kármán and LeMay also established its structure. Hap Arnold appointed the members, who met twice a year. Its leadership consisted of a civilian chairman, paired with the headquarters director of R&D, who sat in an ex-officio capacity. Thirty of the nation's best experts sat on five panels: aircraft and propulsion; missile guidance; fuels, explosives, and nuclear power; radar, communications, and weather; and aeromedicine. A vice-chairman headed each of the committees. Kármán controlled the workings of the group through quarterly meetings of an executive board, comprised of himself, LeMay, and the five vice-chairs. This inner circle nominated members, drafted policy, and appointed ad hoc panels.[13]

Just as everything appeared set for Kármán's council to be convened, a series of events almost destroyed his concept of the peacetime scientific role. The advisory group charter expired in February 1946, and, unfortunately, Hap Arnold retired from the service during the same month. The general failed to recover from his heart attack and left Washington for his ranch in Sonoma, California. Kármán soon realized how important his support had been. General Spaatz, Arnold's successor, had an interest in aeronautical research, but not the passion of his predecessor. In the breach, LeMay stepped forward, seeking to accomplish what had been denied previously. Five weeks after Arnold's retirement, Spaatz sent notices to several dozen leading American scientists, asking them to serve as paid consultants to the newly established Scientific Advisory Board of the Air Forces Commanding General. Already, however, its name was a misnomer. Between Arnold's departure and Spaatz's letter, LeMay engineered the transfer of the board to his R&D directorate, where it would advise *him,* not the commanding general, of advanced research trends, levels of R&D funding, and laboratory facilities. The scientists who received the invitations must have detected the shifting winds; it mentioned LeMay prominently, but said nothing about Theodore von Kármán, the man who invented the board and whom they looked to for science leadership.[14]

The Boss knew the advisory board would fail as a mere bureaucratic appendage. Without direct access to Spaatz, it lacked the prestige and independence necessary to influence policy. Yet he took hope from the position of the War Department hierarchy, which concurred with Arnold's position on civilian science. Army Chief of Staff Gen. Dwight D. Eisenhower stated frankly and publicly, "the armed forces could not have won the war alone. Scientists . . . contributed techniques and weapons which enabled us to outwit and overwhelm the enemy." Eisenhower made plain to his subordinates the peacetime importance of integrating civilian and military knowledge, not just to familiarize the Armed Forces with recent scientific developments, but to include in the planning process "all the civilian resources which can contribute to the defense of the country."[15]

With this reassurance, Kármán flew to California, in need of rest and the companionship of old friends. Here, as in bygone days, he and Pipö animated South Marengo Avenue, and during spring again became familiar faces on the Cal Tech campus. They returned to Washington in June and in mid-month Kármán chaired the first meeting of the Scientific Advisory Board. That day, he must have been struck by a sharp irony. There in a Pentagon conference room sat the most brilliant aeronautical minds in the country, hand-picked by him, many serving only because of his presence. Men the stature of Enrico Fermi, William Pickering, Charles Stark Draper, and Lee A. DuBridge graced the meeting. Yet Kármán's superiors had given him no projects or controversies to lay before the panel. At the close of the sessions, the members felt they had been called to Washington merely to ratify Air Forces science policy, rather than render insight on it. Despite protests from Spaatz and LeMay, Kármán realized the board lacked any opportunity to make "positive contributions" to the air power establishment. This situation forced him to spend much of his precious time "arguing the merits of maintaining the Scientific Advisory Board as a meaningful and active group within the Air Force, and not as a showpiece or letterhead of elder statesmen."[16] The predicament worsened steadily through September 1947, during which month Congress established the National Military Establishment, creating the United States Air Force as a separate military service, coequal to the Army and Navy.

Freed from Army pressure to maintain civilian science, the leaders of the new Air Force considered abolishing the board only weeks after achieving independence. In fact, while Kármán was on an extended holiday in Paris, his secretary found herself warding off raiders from the R&D directorate who tried to seize his office and her desk! Things also began to turn sour at Wright Field. Many officers there resented outsiders with little or no Air Force experience influencing high-level R&D policy. Finally, several members of the advisory board resigned to protest its moribund status. Major Ted Walkowicz, by now one of Kármán's closest friends, pleaded with the chairman to come home and fight for civilian science in the Air Force. Walkowicz reminded him of the group's invaluable service during World War II. He admitted there had been a recent tendency to ignore its suggestions, but asked Kármán not to lose heart. "If you let them shove the [board] down into an unimportant position, the whole future becomes very glum. If the pilots reign supreme in peace time as they do in war time," Walkowicz warned, "the whole cause will be lost . . . and the . . . tragic course of any future war will be decided long before the first shot is fired." Many technically trained junior officers agreed with this assessment. They looked to Kármán and his associates for a jolt of scientific and institutional innovation and depended on Kármán to invigorate the Air Force technological outlook.[17]

The Boss returned to Washington in spring 1948 refreshed and ready to join the battle. One fact augured well for his success. Curtis LeMay had been replaced as R&D director by the more sympathetic Maj. Gen. Laurence C. Craigie. Kármán held long talks with Craigie and suggested terminating the advisory board if its continued existence was at odds with the will of the headquarters. The general rejected this idea. He and Kármán then arrived at a unified position: an independent Air Force required scientific advice at the highest level. They presented this view to Spaatz early in April 1948, suggesting the board be responsible solely to the chief of staff of the Air Force, and that Craigie and future Air Staff R&D directors serve as the panel's military director. Carl Spaatz still retained an open mind on research and development and, at an April 15 meeting with Kármán and Craigie, accepted the chairman's arguments for a robust board of scientists attached organizationally to his office.

The arrangement was promulgated on May 14, 1948, in Air Force Regulation 20-30, which essentially restored those powers agreed upon by Kármán and LeMay in January 1946. The directorate of R&D lost all intermediary control of the board, including staffing, which Spaatz decided to supply from his own personnel pool. Kármán's creation finally won its intended institutional role with a headquarters directive instructing Air Staff offices "cooperate with and aid the Board in their mission of advising and keeping the Chief of Staff informed on all scientific matters."[18]

These actions had the desired effect of restoring vigor to the advisory board. But perhaps even more important was the appointment in September 1948 of Brig. Gen. Donald L. Putt to the R&D directorate. Like Arnold, Putt met Kármán during the GALCIT days. Unlike Arnold, Donald Putt had been the Boss's student at Cal Tech, where he received a master's degree in aeronautical engineering. Like many other pupils, Donald Putt knew Kármán intimately and fell under his influence. He attended the weekly seminars and the lectures. He also experienced the rousing parties at South Marengo when the Hungarian and his family were in peak form. During the war, Putt served as chief of the Experimental Bombardment Aircraft Branch at Wright Field and managed the group that fitted B-29 bombers with the first atomic weapons. In this assignment, and as deputy chief of the Air Materiel Command's engineering division, he assembled a cadre of scientifically trained officers he called his "Junior Indians."[19]

Before Putt reported to the Pentagon, he underwent knee surgery at Walter Reed Hospital, and a number of his young assistants visited him during recuperation. They discussed means to invigorate not only the advisory board, but Air Force R&D in general. They brought Kármán into their confidence and hatched a plan. The chairman would convene a meeting of the board in April 1949, at which time the new chief of staff, Gen. Hoyt S. Vandenberg, would speak. Ted Walkowicz would write the general's welcoming address, the end of which asked the science advisers to review the Air Force research organization and issue a report on improving its structure. But would the chief of staff follow the script? Luckily, Vandenberg canceled his appearance and on April 7, Vice Chief Gen. Muir S. Fairchild, an ardent supporter of long-range research, read the text as written. Vandenberg, like Spaatz before him, had no preconceived ideas on R&D, but would require persuasion before falling in line with Kármán, Putt, and their friends.

Once Fairchild empowered the study, the Boss took over the plotting. He selected Dean Louis N. Ridenour of the University of Illinois to chair an ad hoc panel on Air Force R&D structures. He also persuaded Lt. Gen. James H. Doolittle, hero of the Tokyo raids and a Ph.D. in electrical engineering, to join the group. Kármán knew Ridenour wanted a more prominent role for science in the Air Force and counted on Doolittle's close association with Vandenberg to win him over to the cause. The chairman's alter ego, Frank Wattendorf, also sat on the committee, helping steer the deliberations in the direction desired by the "conspirators."

The Ridenour panel met during summer 1949 and issued its bold findings in September. They offered no surprises to Kármán or Putt: a separate Air Force command for research and development; a headquarters deputy chief of staff for development; and a unified Air Force research budget. In short, Ridenour and his colleagues proposed what Kármán had suggested in *Science, the Key to Air Supremacy:* a technical establishment free of the Air Materiel Command and the deputy chief of staff for materiel in the Pentagon. If this was acted upon, procurement and research would no longer cohabit the same institutions.

Naturally, formidable opposition arose to the Ridenour plan, especially from the materiel community. Moreover, shrinking postwar budgets meant every dollar spent for research would have to be taken from other activities. Nonetheless, Doolittle persuaded Vandenberg to recognize R&D and Fairchild presented the plan to the Air Staff Council on January 2, 1950. Every man present but Putt voted against the proposals, but Fairchild would not be deterred. The following day he announced their implementation and on January 23, 1950, both the Research and Development Command and the Air Staff Deputy Chief of Staff for Research and Development came into being.[20]

Thus, in five short years, Kármán not only presented extraordinary predictions on the future of air power science, but, almost against the will of the Air Force, he established a flourishing board of permanent science advisers and conjured organizational entities to carry out research and development for military aeronautics.

Clearly, by late middle age, Theodore von Kármán had become one of the world's great figures in aeronautics. He had even eclipsed Ludwig Prandtl, discredited for collaborating with the Nazis and outmatched by Kármán's knack for organization. Only gradually, however, did his new status become recognized. Enthusiasm for his work and a joy in living rendered him younger than his chronological age. As a result, the Hungarian temporarily cheated seniority and delayed assuming Prandtl's mantle.

But he could only postpone the inevitable. The first indications of his succession occurred just after the war, when trophies, medals, and plaques started to pour in. British scientists honored Kármán in May 1946 by naming him a member of the Royal Society. Among the Cal Tech faculty, only Robert A. Millikan was so distinguished. The next month the U.S. War Department awarded him the Presidential Medal for Merit, America's highest wartime civilian decoration. General Carl Spaatz, who presided at the ceremonies, especially praised his leadership in forging *Toward New Horizons* and founding the Air Force Scientific Advisory Board. Early in 1947 a panel representing the main disciplines of American engineering presented him with the John Fritz Medal, the most prestigious engineering honor of his adopted homeland, for "his many applications of mathematical and physical theory to the sound solution of engineering problems." He also received Britain's equivalent tribute, the Lord Kelvin Gold Medal for engineering science, won previously by such notables as Guglielmo Marconi, Sir Frank Whittle, and physics Nobel laureate J. J. Thomson. In 1948 the Franklin Institute of Philadelphia bestowed upon him its greatest honor, the Franklin Gold Medal. Finally, the Boss accepted the Air Force Association's Annual Science Trophy. "It is virtually impossible," the citation truthfully declared, "to find a branch of aeronautics in which Dr. von Kármán has not taken a major, active interest."[21]

As these awards, as well as eight honorary doctorates, piled up, the fact of his new role could not be denied, even by Kármán himself. In March 1949 he made his first compromise with the passage of time. Painful though it must have been, he resigned the leadership of two of his most important creations: the Guggenheim Aeronautical Laboratory and the Jet Propulsion Laboratory. Clark Millikan, who had acted for him in both capacities since late 1944, now assumed the positions of GALCIT director and chairman of the JPL executive board. Kármán retained sentimental connections to Cal Tech as professor of aeronautics and adviser to these two famous laboratories. The following May, friends in the Air Force laid plans for a gala seventieth-birthday celebration for the Boss. A year-long discussion ensued about how and where to commemorate his achievements. The party finally occurred in May 1951. Chief of Staff Vandenberg lent his prestige and an impressive guest list drawn from the three services, Cal Tech, and many universities paid homage to the scientist. Truly, the ascent to three-score and ten fused dean of aeronautics to the Kármán name.[22]

But veneration led the Hungarian to action, not complacency. Loaded with honors, freed from Cal Tech, and satisfied with the Scientific Advisory Board, he looked for a suitable opportunity. Kármán wanted to base himself in Europe, especially Paris, a city he loved since student days and his intermittent home since completing *Toward New Horizons*. The chairman first turned his mind to the problem during the European tour for Hap Arnold. All the human and material devastation he witnessed called forth his old belief in international cooperation as a force for goodwill and progress. The pooling of aeronautical knowledge among the Allied nations might be a step in this direction. Kármán experimented with the idea in 1948 when he approached colleagues in several West European countries to collaborate on a series of texts on high-speed aerodynamics, jet propulsion, and other subjects related to aviation science. He met with little success. The famine and dislocation of postwar Europe killed the spirits of countless scientists, many of whom found themselves without jobs or hope.

A course of action presented itself to Kármán early in April 1949. He read one day about a new alliance being forged by twelve western European nations, known as the North Atlantic Treaty Organization (NATO). Kármán saw in this event a chance to hasten scientific exchange and bolster western defense against Soviet expansion. He seized on the Air Force Scientific Advisory Board structure as a means to further these ends: Why not erect a permanent NATO panel of eminent technical experts to counsel the alliance and disseminate discoveries to all participating governments? In short, the Boss set his sights on a European Scientific Advisory Board. He first broached the idea to Deputy

Secretary of Defense Robert A. Lovett, who advised him to seek the support of Gen. Alfred M. Gruenther, Supreme Commander of Allied Forces in Europe. The scientist met the general in Paris during summer 1950, on a fact-finding visit for Hoyt Vandenberg on NATO aeronautical research. Guenther backed the concept, provided that the proposed group confine itself to air power research and development. Kármán had in mind a broader framework, but accepted the ground rules.[23]

He then turned his appeals to the U.S. Air Force and won the support of William Burden, special assistant for R&D to Air Force Secretary Thomas K. Finletter. Burden's interest in aeronautics dated from the 1930s, but he and Kármán had only met recently and became friends. With Burden's endorsement, the Boss could persuade others. The Hungarian continued his Pentagon diplomacy, selling the idea to Maj. Gen. Gordon Saville, the headquarters deputy chief of staff for development. He ended his missionary work in the office of Hoyt Vandenberg, "explor[ing] the problem of using European science for common defense." Here he made another convert, who in turn persuaded the NATO Standing Group (a Washington-based board of generals and admirals representing the United States, France, and the United Kingdom) to approve Air Force sponsorship of a conference of European scientists.

Kármán, Frank Wattendorf, and the advisory board secretariat worked through fall and winter 1950 to prepare for the meeting. In February 1951 letters reached the directors of all the major European aeronautical research institutes, inviting them to the Pentagon to discuss "Mobilization of Scientific Effort in Western European Countries." Shortly afterward, technical leaders from eight nations convened under Kármán's chairmanship. He described for them the workings of the Air Force Scientific Advisory Board, and proposed a parallel European institution, which he called the NATO Advisory Group for Aeronautical Research and Development (AGARD). Emboldened by Kármán's vision of international cooperation and scientific renewal, the conferees adjourned their final session with a clear definition of AGARD's role: to "review advances in aeronautical science, exchange important information, and recommend how the scientific talents within NATO could best be employed in strengthening overall technical ability to solve mutual defense problems."[24]

Yet, high hurdles stood in the way of AGARD. Before becoming a reality, the multinational standing group needed to ratify the new organization. Even more difficult, so did the military staffs of *all* the twelve NATO signatories. Kármán hoped his U.S. Air Force friends would succeed in pressing the standing group to act quickly; but the proposal languished there for months, almost until the end of 1951. He was amazed to learn AGARD had been stalled because of a classic interservice spat. During this period, a pair of American admirals—Forrest P. Sherman and William M. Fechteler—succeeded one another as representatives to the standing group. As successive chiefs of naval operations, they also served on the Joint Chiefs of Staff, which would cast a vote on the advisory group's fate. Kármán discovered that one of these men had used his influence on the NATO group to block debate on AGARD. To clear the obstruction, the Boss exercised another personal contact. He visited Secretary of the Navy Daniel Kimball and asked him to tame the rogue admiral. Kimball, a former president of Aerojet Engineering and a great admirer of Kármán through years of association in California, promised to break the impasse.

Several days later, Kimball received an explanation for the Navy's opposition to AGARD. On one hand, he was told, they feared the project might fail; but far worse, said one admiral, "it could be a major success, in which case I can't let the Air Force [sponsor] it." Kimball quashed the parochial view and the standing group approved AGARD a few days later. More weeks passed while each of the NATO high commands scrutinized the plans. In the meantime, Kármán agreed to two new stipulations: the scientists would only treat unclassified subjects; and the Air Force would support AGARD on an experimental basis through 1953, after which time it would be operated by NATO.[25]

Once the proposal received the backing of all the NATO governments, it returned to the standing group for a final review. On January 24, 1952, almost a full year after Kármán organized the preliminary advisory group meeting in Washington, the NATO commanders announced the formal creation of AGARD. They appointed the U.S. Air Force their executive agent during the first twenty-four months. The European generals asked Vandenberg to select an American citizen to lead the new institution and establish a headquarters in Paris, where the first chairman would serve a two-year term. Thereafter, his successors would be elected annually by the AGARD members. Writing to Kármán on March 5, the Air Force chief of staff deemed it "most fitting that you head [AGARD] in its initial stage." The Boss agreed to carry out the duties he had already assumed.

During the winter of 1952, Kármán spent weeks in the French capital fashioning an aeronautical entity from the materials at hand. Frank Wattendorf followed him to France and Vandenberg assigned Burton Mills, an air technical liaison officer in the Paris air attach's office, to lend assistance. They were joined in spring by Air Force colonels Paul Dane and John J. Driscoll, as well as Kármán's highly able personal assistants, American June Merker and Frenchman Roland Willaume. This group undertook all the mundane labors required to erect AGARD. In addition, three Parisian scientists, professors Joseph Pérès, Maurice Roy, and J. Gérardin, "greatly aided" efforts to root the institution in French soil.

Kármán may have achieved his aim of living in Paris, but many months elapsed before he could relax and enjoy his adopted city. First, AGARD needed such fundamentals as offices, typewriters, even stationery. Before receiving his orders from Washington, Commander of United States Air Forces in Europe Gen. Lauris Norstad gave Kármán all the essentials of supply and equipment. Once the staff had been organized, however, there remained "considerable pressure from continental nations to start the work." But inevitable delays occurred as the NATO governments struggled to select and approve qualified representatives. Complicating this process, the Office of Naval Research and the fledgling Air Research and Development Command sent recruiters to Europe, eager to sign talented scientists to Navy and Air Force contracts. Kármán denounced these efforts, fearing they would deplete the pool of good minds for AGARD and NATO. Worse still, he and his associates faced a May deadline for the first planning sessions of the new group; any later would impinge on summer, when professors left on research trips. After the conference would come the hardest work of all, forming scientific panels and staffing them with the ablest people available.[26]

In April 1952, AGARD opened its offices in NATO headquarters, at the Palais de Chaillot. By then the meeting of the first general assembly had been set for May 19–21, posing a heavy workload for the Boss and his small staff. Yet he felt buoyed up and "thrilled to see the enthusiasm with which the entire scheme was being greeted." He was about to realize once more the fulfillment of his own, and his father's, dream of cooperation among the scholars of many nations. In this case, practice exceeded promise. Eleven countries sent delegates to Paris, and under Kármán's chairmanship, they endorsed the structure copied from

Scientific Advisory Board experience. He then supervised elections for an executive board which, in turn, established four panels: combustion, aeromedicine, flight testing, and wind tunnel technology. Once selected, experts in each field would serve on the committees without compensation (except travel reimbursement). Finally, the assembly voted to staff the Paris office with a separate, full-time secretariat for each of the four technical fields identified at the meeting.

When the Boss banged his gavel on the last session, he knew exactly how to breath life into AGARD; he must recreate the Air Force Scientific Advisory Board. Constant telephone conversations, correspondence, and personal visits built up the AGARD panel memberships during summer 1952. His professional stature lured many able but skeptical onlookers to the fold. To give direction to the initial activities, he placed himself on the roster of some panels, sat as an observer on others, and offered generous counsel wherever needed. In a true sense, the Boss was deeply and personally involved in all aspects of AGARD's early programs and projects. Through the AGARDOGRAPH series of technical monographs, he devised a means of disseminating the advisory group's proceedings and its members' scientific discoveries. He helped organize technical symposia on special subjects and assisted in distributing the resulting reports and manuals. Kármán lent his own prestige to these new scholarly vehicles, publishing articles on aerothermochemistry, a term he coined for the science of combustion phenomena. The Hungarian also opened the talent of the AGARD panels to the consulting needs of the NATO governments. These various strategies to place air power research at the service of the Alliance exceeded even Kármán's sanguine expectations. In short order, the advisory group exerted "a profound and ever-growing influence on the development of aeronautical science and technology in the Western world."[27]

At the end of the two-year trial period, AGARD received its most important endorsement of all: the standing group removed it from U.S. Air Force control and accorded it permanent status on the NATO staff. Each year thereafter, in such diverse places as Copenhagen, Ottawa, Athens, and Istanbul, AGARD held its annual meetings. On every occasion its members elected and re-elected Theodore von Kármán their chairman. More than any of the other institutions he founded, this one bore his personal stamp, his cosmopolitan personality. He had learned internationalism at his father's knee and over the years became one of its most deft practitioners. In AGARD he raised science above national passions, concentrating his friends and colleagues on personal goodwill and "working level" problems. Few but the Boss possessed the scientific reputation, diplomatic sense, and multilingual dexterity to launch and sustain AGARD.[28] Just as he had erected the Scientific Advisory Board for the American Air Force, Kármán secured for aeronautical science a permanent seat in the counsels of the Western alliance.

CHAPTER 8

# The Elder Statesman

Despite the AGARD achievement, a long shadow fell over Kármán's triumph in Paris. Halfway through the long year in which he awaited a decision by the standing group, he experienced the most painful episode of his life, surpassing even the death of this parents. Late in June 1951 his sister Josephine suffered a heart attack after embarking on a trip from New York. On July 2 she succumbed in Pasadena. The loss devastated Kármán. Pipö's end came suddenly, but she had been ill for some time, especially between the summer of 1947 and winter 1948. Yet her decline in no way prepared Theodore for the ensuing loneliness and bereavement. She had been not just a hostess and confidante, but the core of his emotional existence. Since their mother's death a decade earlier they had grown even closer than before. Indeed, Kármán made no secret of his devotion. On travels in which Josephine could not be present, he always packed her picture in his valise, and placed it on his bedstand as soon as he reached his destination. In a nightly ritual of homage, Kármán ended the day by kissing her image. Clearly, her death

> was a terrible shock. Little Pipö was not only my last family link to the past. She was also the organizer of the day-to-day details of my life, the sharer of my inmost feelings. She knew with uncanny instinct when to keep me free from interruption while I was immersed in scientific work, and when to open the gates to entertainment and gaiety. I never realized until she was gone how close we were to each other and how much I depended on her. For weeks I felt lost and lonely. There were times when in my grief I thought I would never return to work, and I am sure that my friends felt that AGARD would be stillborn.[1]

The loss plunged Kármán into a long period of melancholy. Friends and students gauged the impact of her death, and their worst fears were realized. For weeks he suffered a state of physical exhaustion and became almost incapacitated. Some felt he might die. Yet many rallied to his side, taking precautions that he always had company to "soothe the grief." Gradually, the heavy demands of forging AGARD raised him from the torpor, and Kármán recovered; but he never completely regained his former vitality. He first hired Marie Roddenberry, a matronly New Englander and former secretary, to run the household. Kármán then took steps to memorialize Pipö. To commemorate her love of Iberian painters, he underwrote the publication of a multivolume series that reproduced some of the gifted but lesser known artists of Spain. Further in her honor, he sponsored an annual prize for the finest creations by a member of the Spanish Fine Arts Academy.

The Boss also acted to fill the emotional void left by Josephine's passing. During his early years at Aachen, he had befriended George Talbot, a local railway coach and carriage manufacturer of some wealth. The young professor thought he might make money producing glider aircraft and persuaded the businessman to invest in the enterprise. Talbot doubted the wisdom of the scheme, but he and his family liked Kármán and one check followed another. He even set aside a portion of one of his factories for glider construction. As Talbot predicted, the business failed, but with no hard feelings; the industrialist simply counted the loss as a gift to Aachen aeronautics. A long-term outgrowth of this warm connection was a special fondness that developed between the Hungarian and Talbot's wife, Barbel. Aristocratic and graceful, she retained contact with him as the decades went by. So long as Pipö lived, no other woman could cross his path. But with her death, a change took place. Now unattached, Barbel Talbot and Theodore von Kármán resumed their earlier friendship. Once he settled in Paris, she became a steady companion, a romantic interest, and a travel mate. To the extent possible, she served as a surrogate sister and helped palliate the loneliness of his advancing years.[2]

During the horrible period after Josephine died, Kármán learned the limits of his own strength. The arduous labors to erect the NATO advisory group provided a further warning. In the succeeding months he found it increasingly difficult to balance AGARD on one continent and the Scientific Advisory Board on the other. During 1953 and 1954 he managed barely to do both. Even though his appearances in Washington became less frequent, the intellectual and administrative demands of the U.S. Air Force remained great. Searches to fill the rotational board vacancies required constant attention and considerable correspondence. Inevitably, he became enmeshed in planning the group's twice-yearly general as well as executive and ad hoc meetings. Despite the alert administration of acting chairman Gen. Jimmy Doolittle, Kármán could not ignore these conferences, which entailed long, tiring transatlantic flights in fall 1952 and spring 1953 and 1954. Moreover, as new scientific opportunities presented themselves, the Boss expended much time preparing the board to profit from them. For instance, on the advice of Jimmy Doolittle, Kármán appointed a nuclear weapons panel. Its establishment, in turn, involved him in a study on nuclear reactor–powered hydrogen rockets.

Kármán finally decided to leave the Scientific Advisory Board in 1954. The thought probably occurred to him that year, during a planned trip to the United States. Starting in January he would travel from Boston to Washington, then arrive in California, and fly home to Paris at the end of March. He became seriously ill in Pasadena, however, and was confined to his home under a doctor's care. Clearly, Kármán was no longer up to such rigors. The trip represented a farewell to a life on both continents; henceforth, he would be a visitor in his adopted country. The time had come to sever official ties to the last U.S. institution he founded and directed—his final American brainchild. On September 17, 1954, he wrote to Air Force Chief of Staff Gen. Nathan F. Twining, admitting what others had noticed for some time: the simultaneous burden of the two advisory groups "represent an undue strain on my health." He chose to retain the NATO position, partly because of the allure of Paris, but also because the Air Force group had "many excellent members," while AGARD "still needs my active participation."

The Boss and the Air Force had an emotional parting. Kármán confessed he "cherished the memory of many episodes of . . . working for General Arnold" and deemed it "a great privilege to serve" U.S. air power. Twining responded with equal gratitude and named Kármán chairman emeritus of the advisory board, allowing his name to continue to grace the organization. The Air Force also paid tribute to the Hungarian by presenting him the Wright Brothers Memorial Trophy at a special Washington dinner held in his honor just before the Christmas holidays. Finally, his old companion and student Donald Putt (now Lieutenant General Putt) commissioned a portrait artist to paint Kármán's picture during his next visit to New York.[3]

Nathan Twining's appointment of Kármán to emeritus status proved more than an empty honor. It allowed the general, his successors, and other R&D leaders an open door to the scientist's technical and institutional wisdom. Indeed, future board chairmen would seek his counsel both on critical panel appointments and on the most vexing scientific problems. On the other hand, the title conferred several advantages on Kármán. He kept his position as a high-ranking Air Force employee, retaining access to secretarial and other administrative services, as well as reimbursement for government-related travel. More important, the ongoing relationship allowed the Boss to retain his top-secret security clearance, a useful tool in his efforts to cross-fertilize American and European aeronautical developments. Kármán also accepted a fee of fifty dollars per day for consulting services rendered on a virtual year-round basis.

In recognition of his continued informal contributions to U.S. air power, on June 20, 1956, a crowd of one thousand aviation dignitaries attended a testimonial dinner in Los Angeles honoring Theodore von Kármán with the Presidential Medal of Freedom. The audience not only saluted him for winning the nation's highest peacetime award for civilians, but for a belated celebration of his seventy-fifth birthday.[4]

Just as he accepted these tributes, Kármán found himself drawn back into the Air Force orbit. An active consultancy would not do. Try as he might to diminish the relationship, a winding path led him once more toward a major Air Force project. Kármán's renewed affiliation began around the time he decided to retire from the Scientific Advisory Board. The idea originated with Donald Putt. As the commander of the Air Research and Development Command, Putt discovered serious deficiencies in long-range research and development planning. He first raised these matters in a meeting of the advisory board, and later with Gen. Laurence Craigie, another Kármán alumnus and now the Air Staff deputy chief of staff for development. Putt believed the existing forecasts lacked vision, treating scientific and technical developments only in the near-term. This failure led to timidity in designing new aircraft and subsystems; to incremental, rather than revolutionary, advances; and, ultimately, to "qualitative mediocrity" in future systems. To return foresight to aeronautical thinking, Putt asked Craigie to launch the advisory board on a broad, forward-looking report.

What we need is an intensive long term look at the capabilities of those technical areas which will contribute most to the development of Air Force equipment in the next ten plus years. The "Toward New Horizons" type of study executed by the Scientific Advisory Board after World War II is the kind now needed. This study, estimating further technical trends while remaining remarkably valid in some technical areas during the interval since it was written, needs to be reviewed periodically in view of the rapid progress that is made in many other areas.[5]

Craigie reacted immediately. He dispatched Chester Hasert, the board's executive secretary, to Paris to confer with the AGARD chairman. Hasert reported the results of his discussions during the first week of December 1953. Putt must have been disappointed. Revisiting *Toward New Horizons* "met with [Kármán's] very cautious and somewhat reserved reaction. He sees many dangers in such long range forecasts, thinks they are only guesses and there will be too much personal prejudice." He raised fewer objections to revising and modernizing *Toward New Horizons,* and suggested an exhaustive search of the technical literature. In reality, Kármán's principal dislike of Putt's proposal had less to do with the risk of failure than his own reduced physical vigor. "The Boss," wrote Hasert, "is very tired these days, and may not be able to contribute too much of his energy." For the same reason he decided to quit the Scientific Advisory Board, he also declined to lead a full-scale projection of air power technology.

The following month Kármán discussed the problem at a Washington meeting of the board's executive committee. Once again, he refused to undertake a new version of *Horizons.* This time he argued that the "limitations intrinsic in a part-time Advisory Board [make it] inadvisable . . . to undertake the extensive and comprehensive effort." Aeronautical and astronautical research had expanded greatly since 1945, beyond the scrutiny of a single board of "wise men." Moreover, Kármán reflected on the special conditions prevailing at the end of the war. In those days, scientists spoke freely with one another, glad the hostilities had ended and eager to exchange ideas. But the Cold War raised international tensions and destroyed the sense of cooperation present at the time of *Toward New Horizons.* The Hungarian suggested Putt and Craigie launch a limited analysis based on the personal observations of the advisory board's committee chairmen. This study could be followed by "a continuing series of studies on a modest scale."[6]

Unfortunately for Kármán, the memory of *Toward New Horizons*—of a truly comprehensive survey—could not be banished so easily.

Early in spring 1954 Air Force R&D leaders gathered near Fort Monroe, at Old Point Comfort, Virginia, to hear the panel chairs present impressionistic reports of the kind recommended by the Boss in January. Kármán himself was absent. Under the familiar banner "New Horizons," the studies treated explosives and armaments, geophysics, aeromedical research, aircraft, reconnaissance, fuels and propulsion, intelligence systems, social sciences, nuclear weapons, and electronics communications. Brief and general, these analyses only whetted Putt's appetite for a true, long-range forecast, and many on the board agreed with him. In an odd turn of events, just after the Old Point Comfort meeting, the executive committee reconvened and voted to appoint a select group of outstanding *young* researchers to draft an analysis of future aeronautical trends. They would work under the guidance of the board's senior scientists. The committee imposed an impossibly short deadline of summer 1954.

But in Princeton the following June, the panel chairmen reconsidered their decision to have junior scholars write a long-range projection. The turnabout stemmed from Kármán's continued resistance to the project. Chester Hasert had again flown to Paris to test the waters, and once more found the Boss "very lukewarm." He struck to his view that the board should not undertake a sequel to his famous report and told Hasert he had supported the limited forecasts only "because he thought that was what the Board wanted."

Kármán's stubborn opposition, still based fundamentally on a personal desire to reduce his Air Force involvement, finally seemed to scuttle Putt's initiative. In September 1954, fewer than forty copies of the Old Point Comfort reports were distributed to Air Force personnel, with all mention of "New Horizons" expunged from the text. Later that month, Jimmy Doolittle gave more bad news to Donald Putt, now deputy chief of staff for development. Citing the very reasons Kármán put forth over the past year, the board declined to act on Putt's request for an updated *Toward New Horizons*.[7]

Yet, the issue refused to die. Putt's successor at the Air Research and Development Command, Gen. Thomas Power, pressed the cause. He discovered the same essential flaw in R&D planning as his predecessor: no long-range vision. In 1955 Power sought to correct this deficiency by appointing six generals to head committees on the principal aeronautical technologies: missiles, propulsion, aircraft, electronics, materials, and aerosciences. Scientists from the Air Force Office of Scientific

Research and the Air Research and Development Command staffed the panels and completed the reports within a year. As Power had allowed each group to choose its own methodology, his staff faced a difficult task forging one coherent study from six disparate ones. In fact, in 1956 they finally threw up their hands in defeat. At this point, Brig. Gen. Bernard A. Schriever, a former aide to Donald Putt and presently chief of the Air Force ballistic missile program, proposed one more attempt to persuade the Boss to direct a comprehensive assessment of Air Force science. If Putt had failed to win over the senior scientist, perhaps one of his young R&D proégés would succeed. Schriever cleverly eliminated one of Kármán's best-known objections. Since the advisory board lacked the capacity or will to undertake the job, Schriever recommended General Power launch the review through the National Academy of Sciences. The Navy had already proved the efficacy of the concept with its 1956 Project NOBSKA (Polaris Missile) study, produced under contract by the academy.[8]

General Power and Jimmy Doolittle brought the suggestion to Dr. Detlev Bronk, president of the National Academy. Bronk had two reasons to be sympathetic: as a Navy pilot during World War I, he understood the needs of military aviation; and he had long known and admired Theodore von Kármán. Talks between the president and the two generals went smoothly and at a November 8, 1956, meeting of the academy's governing council, a vote was taken to accept an Air Force contract for a second *Toward New Horizons*. Power's preliminary forecasts of R&D would form the technical backbone, and Project NOBSKA the administrative prototype. Bronk pledged his institution would "review the work that has been done by the Air Force Committees and . . . bring a fresh and more detached point of view to the formulation of problems and possible paths to their solution." Though unenthusiastic, the Boss realized he could no longer resist the call to duty. The bargain struck among Bronk, Power, and Doolittle rested on Kármán's participation, and during a brief visit to Washington in spring 1957, he let himself be talked into the chairmanship. He accepted with some testiness. "The Air Force," he complained, "liked to think that we scientists could read the future, and they had come to like the idea of grandiose speculation."[9] With that, the Hungarian ended his brief semi-retirement from American air power.

Kármán may have been a reluctant leader, but he did appreciate the fact that Bronk's organization would handle all the necessary arrangements and details. The academy processed all of its studies in much the same way. Once a national search identified prospective participants from government, industry, and the universities, the staff worked out specifics of date and place, housing, and technical facilities. Like the Polaris project before it, the Air Force forecast would be researched and written at picturesque Woods Hole, adjacent to Falmouth, Massachusetts. Both the renowned Oceanographic Institute and the Marine Biological Laboratory operated there. To attract the greatest number of distinguished scholars, the academy scheduled the sessions during summer, between academic semesters. Since the Power reports opened a vast field of inquiry, the organizers planned a second summer session in 1958.

During the warm months of 1957 the scientists, their wives, and children descended on the quiet seaside town, where beaches, summer theaters, and other recreations abounded. These features pleased their Hungarian host. He approved heartily of the "amiable inefficiency" of meeting at such a lovely place, among such a variety of people. After arriving from Europe on Thursday, June 20, 1957, Kármán traveled directly to Woods Hole. He took rooms at the nearby Coonamasset Inn, a short drive from the conference site. The formal deliberations occurred in a fine white house on Church Street, part of a nine-acre waterfront estate. Kármán adapted himself quickly to the relaxed atmosphere and decided to attend sessions not in his usual dark suit and tie, but in a nautical costume of short-sleeved shirt and sailor's cap. The Boss took an instant liking to long dinners with friends at the Landfall Restaurant, which became a regular nightspot as the sessions progressed.[10] No different from his life in Aachen, Pasadena, or Paris, he liked to transact business over food and drink, and much good work resulted from these evenings around the table.

Kármán realized the Woods Hole project would be "a task of far greater magnitude than that which we faced at the end of the last war," so he assembled a small advisory committee to lighten his duties. Dr. H. Guyford Stever, an MIT physicist, agreed to manage daily operations as the project's deputy director. Amiable and youthful, he served as chief scientist of the Air Force during 1955 and 1956 and participated in Kármán's first European mission for Arnold. The director also relied on another young scientist, Dr. Allan Puckett of Hughes Aircraft, as well as his old favorite Hugh Dryden, then the director of the

National Advisory Committee for Aeronautics. Kármán and his three assistants met on June 22 and 23, the weekend before the opening session.

They started with only two hard facts: a $300,000 Air Force contract for the 1957 sessions, and a list of 111 interested scientists. A distinguished group, they represented a national sampling of twenty-six universities, twenty corporations, and eight government agencies. Undoubtedly, the presence of the Boss helped attract men of eminence, such as Harvard astronomer Fred Whipple, Charles Stark Draper of MIT, Nobel laureate Edwin M. McMillan of the University of California, and Joseph Kaplan, director of the U.S. Committee of the International Geophysical Year. Kármán, Stever, Dryden and Puckett assigned the selectees to six committees, which paralleled those of the Power Report. Propulsion, electronics, materials, and aircraft were transferred unchanged. The aerosciences now fell under several subgroups: nuclear and non-nuclear air ordnance, guidance and control, geophysics, aeromedicine, and psychology. Power's missile panel became more broadly focused at Woods Hole, designated guided missiles and space vehicles.[11]

After lunch on Monday, June 24, Kármán called his colleagues to order and inaugurated the first long-range Air Force science forecast in twelve years, known already as the Woods Hole summer studies. He introduced Detlev Bronk and Guyford Stever, who yielded in turn to Donald Putt, a substitute for Air Force Chief of Staff Gen. Nathan Twining. Putt felt satisfaction in realizing a four-year-old dream: a second-generation *Toward New Horizons,* led by Theodore von Kármán. Secretary of the Air Force James H. Douglas rose next to welcome the Hungarian "back [to] the old stand after the distinguished service he rendered in this same sort of project at the end of World War II." The following day the scientists listened to Maj. Gen. Howell M. Estes, Jr., describe the Air Force's R&D objectives as well as its latest aircraft and missiles.[12]

For the rest of the week Kármán and the advisory committee laid out the essential tasks of the Woods Hole endeavor. In 1957, the aim would be to treat subjects broadly and provide quick technical advice to the Air Research and Development Command (ARDC). Late in the summer the chairman and his three assistants would integrate the conclusions in a final report. Then came the struggle to "formulate . . . plans for the more detailed and fundamental studies contemplated for summer of 1958." Toward these ends, Kármán obtained the full cooperation of the Academy of Sciences, the ARDC, and Jimmy Doolittle's Scientific Advisory Board (many of whose members staffed the Woods Hole committees). The Boss told his colleagues to venture as far as twenty-five years into the future, but to start by looking back a dozen years to *Toward New Horizons*. A review of its contents suggested the "wild" predictions of 1957 might seem conservative by 1967. He asked the scientists "to use . . . vision, and not to be afraid of the possibilities to which the imagination can lead." The panelists first convened at the end of June and in the heat of August settled their differences in order to complete the written reports.[13]

Unfortunately, all the foresight in the world could not save Theodore von Kármán and the first Woods Hole Conference from disappointment. The initial blow fell less than a week after the meetings opened, when General Power left his R&D post to lead the Strategic Air Command. Inevitably, his transfer resulted in diminished interest in Woods Hole by ARDC, the forecast's sponsor. Second, the question of proprietary rights stifled open exchange among the scientists. They were required to sign a statement declaring themselves "honor-bound to respect the confidence implicit in disclosure." But the lack of clear legal protection for unique technical concepts inhibited free discussion. By far the worst of all, on October 4, 1957, the USSR launched Sputnik I, the world's first manmade satellite. In one newsflash, the ideas of the first Woods Hole meetings were rendered obsolete. By this time all the contributors had gone home until the next summer, leaving Kármán, his advisory committee, and a few academy staffers to suffer the consequences.

The Boss greeted these events with ambivalence. On one hand, he felt it vindicated his instinct to avoid long-range forecasting. On the other, the Air Force had proven shortsighted. In 1957, the generals warned repeatedly not to place satellites on the Woods Hole agenda. Too visionary, they said. Such discussions might lead powerful Congressmen to accuse the service of coveting big budgets for frivolous hardware. Against his inclination, Kármán acceded to their wishes. Then, on October 5, a frightened public demanded to know "what we scientists had been doing." Even more, what had the *politicians* and *generals* done to prevent U.S. territory from becoming vulnerable to Soviet surveillance or attack? Kármán had no answers, only an outdated report. This he presented to Gen. Samuel Anderson, the new leader of the Air Research and Development Command.[14]

Though frustrated, the Boss decided to see the 1958 session through to completion. Perhaps some credibility could be restored to the undertaking. Meantime, everyone concerned needed a rest. The 1957 report finally grew to 2,800 pages and "to put it mildly the staff was fairly exhausted after spending weekends, nights, and many daylight hours to turn it in." The Woods Hole organizers attended mainly to administrative chores during the winter months of late 1957 and early 1958. In the interim, the Air Force signed another contract with the National Academy of Sciences, agreeing to pay $400,000 for a second forecast. It provided for briefings to Anderson and his staff at the end of December 1958, and the publication of one thousand copies of a summary volume in February 1959. The visiting scientists would again be well compensated for their labors, at the rate of regular salary plus 50 percent. Once more, panelists spending at least thirty consecutive days on the site could lodge their families at the expense of the Air Force. But some aspects differed from 1957. Kármán's former student, William Sears, chairman of the engineering department at Cornell University, agreed after some persuasion by the Boss to replace Guyford Stever as deputy project director. Stever now devoted all his energies to chairing a Scientific Advisory Board ad hoc committee on Air Force technical organization. Its recommendations had profound effects, resulting ultimately in the demise of Air Research and Development Command in April 1961 and the creation of Air Force Systems Command on the same date. As a result, R&D, production, and procurement would be vested in a single air power institution.

Partly because of the manpower requirements of the Stever project, Woods Hole II opened with a significant turnover in personnel. Many fine men, such as Ted Walkowicz, found themselves drafted by Jimmy Doolittle to assist Stever. Hugh Dryden and Allen Puckett, the rest of the original advisory council, left for other assignments. Although about as many people (106) sat on the panels in 1958, only 20 percent of them had participated in the 1957 sessions. Many of the new members were young scientists. Moreover, diminished housing accommodations reduced the number of full-timers to sixty or seventy. Although the academy's administrative machinery continued to operate smoothly, Kármán began with few of the scientists from the year before.[15] In essence, he had to start anew.

Enroute to Paris, the AGARD chairman arrived back in Washington in February 1958. On February 14 and 15 he met General

Anderson, the Woods Hole committee chairmen, and National Academy of Sciences representatives at the R&D command's new headquarters building at Andrews Air Force Base, Maryland.

They decided to hold a three-day preliminary session in Massachusetts the week of June 23, during which time Kármán and Sears planned to draft the project's objectives and make committee assignments. At the formal opening on June 26 and 27, Anderson and other Air Force officials would speak to the scientists on present aeronautical developments and future requirements. Prior to these events, in the spring Kármán conferred again with his panel leaders in Denver. After the discussions at Andrews he thought it wise to learn their thinking before the June opening at Woods Hole. He wanted to make plain to them that the military uses of space should be among the subjects considered carefully during the 1958 sessions. This view was shared by his committee chairmen: by Joseph Charyk on the aircraft, guided missiles, and space vehicles panel; by John H. Holloman and Pol Duwez on materials; by Frank Wattendorf on propulsion; by Charles T. Morgan on life sciences; and by Louis T. E. Thompson on weapons. Indeed, satellites, space platforms, and space-flight vehicles seemed to be the natural centers of attraction in the coming discussions. Propelling these systems into orbit emerged as the second great question, whether by rockets of chemical, nuclear, solar, magnetohydrodynamic, particle, plasma, or radioactive design.[16]

But to the dismay and surprise of his colleagues, the Boss strongly opposed a space-*centered* study. Essentially, he continued to insist on the *Toward New Horizons* approach: a general survey of aeronautical and astronautical trends rather than a report of narrow, purely technical interest. It became for Kármán a philosophical point. By definition, a long-range forecast must have the broadest scope. He made his position clear in letters of welcome to the 1958 contributors.

> While there is no doubt that the era of space flight with its many military and civil implications is at hand, it will be a long time before the foot soldier, the boat, and the airplane vanish completely from the "surface" of the earth. Our initial study last summer reviewed the military applications of earth satellites and . . . outlined for the Air Force certain possibilities in the fields of reconnaissance and communications. These questions . . . should occupy much of our deliberations this year. At the same time, there are still many forward-looking considerations relating to more conventional but no less urgent, aspects of air power which should also receive full and detailed

attention. In thus giving adequate thought to *all* aspects of military possibilities we can do our share to contribute to well balanced and far-reaching research and development programs in support of our national security.[17]

The old Hungarian repeated his admonition again and again, both before and after the start of Woods Hole II. "I believe," he told materials chairman John Holloman a month prior to arriving at Woods Hole, "less emphasis should be given to examining any one weapon system or any particular mission. During this coming summer, I feel we must concentrate more on expanding scientific potentialities and present to the Air Force a report similar to the . . . series which we accomplished for General Arnold in 1945." Kármán continued the attack by soliciting the support of his deputy, William Sears. Though a dear friend, the one-time pupil reminded the Boss of the public statements of General Anderson and other Air Force leaders, expressing an interest *only* in space-oriented research. Sears argued that Anderson should receive a report that mainly proposed space options for U.S. air power. Facts were facts, said Sears. "I think we will have a tough job to convince the Air Force that they are still interested in wings, turbojets and such things. They have apparently decided to become a Space Force."[18]

But, as events proved, the chairman would not be moved. After delivering a paper on June 20 to a fluid mechanics meeting at the University of California–Berkeley, he arrived six days later at Woods Hole for the preparatory sessions. In light of severe pressures from the public and Congress to meet the Sputnik challenge, a tight schedule crowded the months of July and August. Exacting standards of content and format were imposed. The project ended on August 29 and by Labor Day Kármán and Sears expected the draft committee reports. These papers would then be circulated for comment and be consolidated in one volume by the end of October. This work entailed an enormous outpouring of energy, the more so since tentative conclusions needed to be ready on August 14 for a visiting delegation of Air Force officials.[19]

The pressure to hasten Woods Hole II did result in quick production. But, in the final analysis, Kármán succeeded in presenting the report he wanted to write, rather than the one the Air Force wished to receive. The Boss exacted from his committee chairmen a pledge to give satellites and other space systems no more importance than the regular air power subjects. For instance, the flight vehicles panel decided to study strategic warfare, air defense, tactical warfare, logistics, and reconnaissance, but to discuss the space mission only as it related to these five categories. The briefings presented in the lecture room of the National Academy of Sciences building in Washington, D.C., on December 15 and 16, 1958, reflected Kármán's victory. It must have been a slightly bewildering experience for the chiefs of Air Force R&D to hear the committee chairmen read their findings. Though a well-placed Academy of Sciences administrator said the conclusions were "very well received," the absence of the space priority doomed the report to oblivion.[20]

The reconnaissance presentation, for example, did suggest artificial earth satellites to oversee foreign territory. But Dr. Brian O'Brien devoted equal time to low-altitude high-speed aircraft, optical and visual techniques, infrared, electronics, radar, and acoustic detection. Dr. Robert Petersen discussed the weapons and limited warfare conclusions, which included only a hasty mention of space, and more emphasis on short takeoff and landing aircraft, large transports, and air-to-surface fire control. The military uses of space flight segment, led by Dr. Marvin Pitkin, delved into various space systems, but was allotted only fifteen minutes, less than any other briefing but propulsion. Doctors W. Randolph Lovelace and J. C. R. Licklider reviewed the physiology of aircraft pilots and space passengers. But in their talk on men in future Air Force systems, they conceded the panel could not agree on the wisdom of sending humans into orbit. Under R&D facilities, Dr. John R. Markham spoke of the special infrastructure needed for space exploration, but equally described other support problems.

After a short break, the all-important aircraft, guided missiles, and space vehicles report was presented by Dr. Courtland Perkins. He had much less to say about space systems than about nuclear-armed missiles, bombers, and fighters. Only the propulsion panel, chaired by Dr. Frank Wattendorf, dealt mainly (and imaginatively) with the space-related subject of rocketry. Doctors William Pickering and William Shockley led the electronics, guidance, and control committee and devoted their discussion equally to space and to aircraft systems. The materials panel, represented by Dr. John H. Holloman, described the several regimes of heat and radiation acting on future Air Force equipment, but neglected to clarify whether aircraft, missiles, rockets, or spacecraft were his principle concern. Finally, Dr. Frederick Seitz told the audience the conclusions of the general sciences group, which recommended research on a number of subjects, including physics, atmospherics, biology and psychology, mathematics, and chemistry. A space platform, he said, appeared useful only for astronomers and astrophysists.[21]

Clearly, in the Woods Hole summer studies Theodore von Kármán failed to achieve the success of *Toward New Horizons*. The Boss's early and persistent instinct not to undertake another forecast proved well founded. Yet, even though the Air Force would shelve the Woods Hole findings and plunge ahead with its quest for space leadership, Kármán's venture did have a beneficial side-effect. The good relations cemented between the Air Research and Development Command and the National Academy of Sciences during the summers of 1957 and 1958 resulted by 1960 in a permanent relationship between the two organizations. The academy agreed to provide technical advice on an open-ended, contractual basis. It would establish a permanent panel of distinguished scientists to conduct "broad investigations of major problems" for the R&D commander. Much as the Scientific Advisory Board counseled the Air Force chief of staff, the academy's Air Force Studies Board would serve the leaders of the Air Research and Development Command, and subsequently the Air Force Systems Command.

Turning again to AGARD business in Paris, the Boss looked back on the arduous months at Woods Hole with unavoidable disappointment; he could not fail to see the poor reception accorded the sequel to *Toward New Horizons*. But rather than attribute it to philosophical differences with the Air Force on long-range scientific forecasts, Kármán returned to the arguments that made him balk in the first place. "I have a hunch," he admitted, "that inducing scientists to think together in committees may not always prove as productive as some people think. I do not say that all committees aiming to produce horses will eventually create camels, but there is some likelihood that the creative impulse may be submerged." Kármán had learned to respect technical teamwork during his years in America and recognized the importance of specialists exchanging ideas in close collaboration. But he also saw "a tendency to elevate the specialist beyond his place, to the detriment of the man with the overview who can see a pattern among isolated events. In the long run I still think that the finest creative thoughts come not out of organized teams but out of the quiet of one's own world." What could differ more from the "continuous, communal sessions at Woods Hole" than *Science, the Key to Air Supremacy,* drafted by a lone figure in a luxury Paris hotel?[22]

CHAPTER 9

# "His Life Was Full"

Regardless of the long, unhappy experience of first rejecting and then undertaking a science forecast for his American friends, the Boss lived a charmed life in Europe. Indeed, he became a celebrity of sorts. Unable to tolerate as many transatlantic trips, Kármán nonetheless made frequent journeys from his Parisian base to the other Western European capitals. By rail and air he visited every place on the AGARD map. Indeed, during any one year in the mid-1950s he may have been abroad as much as at home. Throughout the continent the elderly Kármán became a familiar lecturer and raconteur, treating his audiences to a persona like the one he showed the generals and admirals: the bemused old Hungarian professor with the conspicuous hearing aid, the rumpled clothes, the black beret, and the Rabelaisian wit. His performance won the hearts of his audiences and opened their minds to more serious subjects. When he appeared as a banquet speaker he often liked to compare his talks to "a lady's dress—short, interesting, and covering the essential points." Kármán also joked frequently about his age. Why did he travel first-class instead of deluxe? After all, for a "mere" seventy dollars more, he would not only receive a steak dinner, but the attentions of an additional stewardess. The answer: "My doctor forbids me the one and I am too old for the other." His talks often counseled patience in research. Crash programs all had the same result: "Instead of making one girl pregnant for nine months, you get nine girls pregnant in one month." More often than not, he fell prey to his own wit. Kármán defined an aerodynamacist as "a man who is willing to assume everything except responsibility."[1]

The popularity of the elder statesman role drew the news media to his appearances, and brought him to the attention of the public at large. The speeches covered in the press stressed the relationship between successful engineering and the fundamental laws of nature. He also urged younger people to resist the obsession of space travel and concentrate on classical aerodynamic theory. Throughout the 1950s Kármán contributed a series of articles to *Interavia,* a popular review of international air and space. Here he touched on such subjects as worldwide cooperation and organization, the technical implications of faster planes and rockets, the future of aerodynamics, the flight characteristics of ballistic and guided missiles, and the American role in space. In 1954 Cornell University Press published his nontechnical textbook on the history of the science of flight, *Aerodynamics: Selected Topics in Light of Their Historical Development.*

The Hungarian's scholarly writings also became grist for newspaper articles and some widely read scientific publications. Through them, the general reader learned of Kármán's interest in a fledgling branch of aerodynamics called aerothermochemistry, or the study of the burning of fuels in a strong, open stream of air—in other words, the phenomena related to jet propulsion. It led Kármán to a theory of the evolution and quenching of flames, and finally to participation in the proceedings of the International Combustion Institute. The old scientist also studied the interaction between flow characteristics and electromagnetic forces, a critical problem of space flight. In fact, he coined the name *magnetofluid-dynamics* for this new field.[2]

Kármán's notoriety also grew in America, reaching its zenith during 1961, his eightieth year. He owed this remarkable acclaim to the Air Force, whose leaders had long since forgotten the vexations of Woods Hole. The tributes began in early May when Sen. Henry Jackson of Washington praised Kármán's scientific contributions, labors for western defense, and inspired teaching. On the occasion of his birthday, the Senate resolved to "express our gratitude to him for great things done and yet to be done." The House of Representatives paid a similar tribute the following week. The U.S. press then picked up the story. Articles from Baltimore to Pasadena recounted his Hungarian ancestry, the Vortex Street, and the relationship with Hap Arnold.

Interest was fanned when Kármán held a press conference the morning of May 9, at Washington's elegant Mayflower Hotel. For an hour the grand old man of aeronautics charmed the reporters with his droll humor and surprising predictions. He said the "missile gap" between the United States and the USSR was not really so serious and America would close it in three to five years. He thought nuclear war unlikely, but talked of deterrence through tank- and truck-based long-range missiles. Kármán predicted America would surpass Soviet men-in-space efforts and equal the Russian spaceships and satellites "in the next few years." The Hungarian felt Commander Alan Shepard's sensational 302-mile suborbital flight just four days earlier proved that the United States had already solved the essential scientific problems of travel outside the atmosphere. Finally, he envisioned a ramjet aircraft capable of entering and leaving earth's orbit on its own power, at a cost far below that of expendable rockets. Kármán's statements flooded the nation's newspapers the following day: "Serious Space Gap Is Doubted"; "Air Breathing Orbital Planes Urged by Expert"; "Missile-Launching Trucks Proposed as Harder to Hit." Clearly, he had scored a triumph. One editorial carried on the wire services likened him to Alan Shepard: the old hero versus the new, the wise man and the brave man. But "without genius," the writer observed, "there would have been little opportunity for courage."[3]

This public acclaim sprang from a day-long symposium and banquet honoring the octogenarian on Thursday, May 11, 1961. The Institute of the Aerospace Sciences, under contract to the Air Force Office of Scientific Research, managed the gala event. Thirty-seven national and international organizations—including AGARD, the National Academy of Sciences, the American Rocket Society, the departments of the Army and Navy, the American Philosophical Society, the Aerospace Industries Association of America, and the American Association of University Professors—cooperated in staging the birthday tribute. On that morning, hundreds packed the Cotillion Room of Washington's Sheraton Park Hotel. Hugh Dryden, now deputy administrator of the National Aeronautics and Space Administration, called the meeting to order to hear papers on two of the Boss's milestone scientific subjects: the buckling of thin shells and the Kármán Vortex Street. During the afternoon, former GALCIT student William Sears chaired the sessions and introduced two other men of long association with the old scientist: Joseph Kaplan from the founding days of the Scientific Advisory Board and Martin Summerfield of the Suicide Club. Kaplan emphasized the honoree's unique contributions to international cooperation. In reply, Kármán joked he had no choice but work for harmony among nations; his students came from every corner of the globe.[4]

Evening brought the celebration's high point. The guests arrived in formal attire and assembled in the hotel's banquet hall to fête Kármán over dinner. Numbered among the seven hundred in attendance were some his closest associates, many military leaders, and several political dignitaries. Personal well-wishers included Aerojet cofounder Andrew Haley, GALCIT partner Clark Millikan, JATO test pilot Homer Boushey, Godfrey McHugh from *Toward New Horizons* days, secretary and housekeeper Marie Roddenberry, student and colleague Frank Wattendorf, and old friend Donald Putt (presently a civilian and chairman of the Air Force Scientific Advisory Board). The uniformed contingent also turned out in force: Gen. Bernard Schriever, first commander of the Air Force Systems Command; Air Force Chief and Vice-Chief of Staff generals Thomas White and Curtis LeMay; and Supreme Allied Commander of NATO Gen. Lauris Norstad. Deputy Secretary of Defense Roswell L. Gilpatric, Navy Secretary John B. Connolly, and Air Force Secretary Eugene M. Zuckert represented the civilian Department of Defense leadership. Three fellow science administrators—Guyford Stever, the chairman-elect of the Scientific Advisory Board; Atomic Energy Commission chairman Glenn T. Seaborg; and Robert C. Seamans, associate director of NASA—joined the celebration. Finally, and most notably, the White House sent Vice-President Lyndon B. Johnson and Dr. Jerome Weisner, the science adviser to President John F. Kennedy.

Toastmaster and fellow Hungarian Edward Teller, the renowned nuclear physicist and early member of the Scientific Advisory Board, introduced the banquet speaker. Undersecretary of the Air Force Joseph V. Charyk, for many years a Kármán associate, described the night's honoree as a man who fostered aeronautics through four qualities: technical genius, a vision of the future, the capacity to counsel, and the gift of leadership. "Only rarely in history," declared Charyk, "does there appear a man possessing all these attributes. When one does appear, the field of that man's endeavor grows dramatically. Its impact on the world is profound." The accolades continued. A delegate from each of the thirty-seven institutions cooperating in the evening read a message of appreciation. Jet Propulsion Laboratory director and GALCIT professor William Pickering announced the American Rocket Society sponsorship of an annual von Kármán lecture series, carrying a one-thousand-dollar honorarium. Teller then read a birthday greeting from President Kennedy, which hailed him as "the country's senior statesman in the field of aerospace science" and recognized his "many contributions not only to our national security and welfare, but also to science. The technical lead which this country engineered," wrote Kennedy, "reflects your sustained efforts." By this time, the hour was late. At the end of a very long day of tribute, the Boss finally rose to cut a huge layered cake. Stepping to the microphone, he knew everyone must be as tired as he. Smiling, Kármán simply asked his well-wishers to go home and go to bed.[5]

After the watershed of his eightieth year, at which he appeared well, the scientist gradually fell victim to the infirmities of age. Yet, he continued in the AGARD chairmanship, which still led him all over Europe. Late in July 1961 he presided over its eleventh general assembly in Oslo, Norway, where he again made headlines. The Boss told reporters that in ten years they would see nuclear-powered rockets and jet aircraft flying to the edge of the atmosphere. The following September he traveled to London to accept the James Watt International Medal from the British Institution of Mechanical Engineers. Thus, his life balanced on the fulcrum of Paris, with AGARD business on one end and a variety of other professional engagements on the other.

The visits to Pasadena continued, but fell to an average of but one month a year. He arrived there in winter 1962 to see companions and colleagues and make an annual pilgrimage to nearby Indio, a desert community where his friends Floyd Odlum and Jacqueline Cochran opened their magnificent ranch to him. Kármán had known the wealthy couple since the 1930s when she won the 1938 Bendix Transcontinental Air Race and broke many aviation speed records. Equally adept at business, she owned a cosmetics manufacturing firm and a chain of beauty parlors. Kármán arrived at the ranch at Christmastime and was received with the usual attentions. But the couple noticed an unhappy change; he had really grown old. His gait was hampered by arthritis and he moved with considerable exertion. These limitations oppressed him. But his mind showed the same nimbleness as ever, and he enjoyed his stay.

On the last day of the year, as Kármán floated in his guests' immense canopied swimming pool, he received a telephone call from Washington. Science adviser Jerome Weisner gave him news that acted like strong medicine: he had won the first National Medal of Science, to be presented by President Kennedy at a White House ceremony. "My, that's nice," said a stunned Kármán.

Yet, in light of the origins of the award, his selection should not have been a great surprise. Congress established the honor in 1959, one of the many outgrowths of the Sputnik debacle. Kennedy appointed a Committee on the Medal of Science and asked Frederick Seitz, president of the National Academy of Science, to be its chairman. The statute permitted up to twenty honorees each year, but Seitz and his colleagues decided just one person should receive the distinction. The Boss not only distinguished himself in basic research, but he had also worked intimately with the Academy of Sciences during Woods Hole, where Sputnik and space dominated the discussions, if not the conclusions. Moreover, Kármán's long and productive leadership of the Suicide Club ranked him one of the founders of U.S. rocketry. Rooted in the Sputnik era and presented by a president committed to men in space, the initial National Science Medal logically went to an aerospace scientist. In that category, none compared to Kármán.[6]

Weisner's news filled him with delight. He had planned to spend all of February in Paris, but quickly revised his itinerary. On the morning of February 18, 1963, the aged Hungarian stood with some forty admirers and associates in the Rose Garden of the White House, awaiting the young president. Luckily, Kármán had bundled up against the Washington chill with a heavy topcoat and scarf. When Kennedy and his assistants arrived, the two men introduced themselves and turned to walk to the reception area. But a set of stairs momentarily halted Kármán, hobbled by painfully arthritic feet. Although Kennedy quickly took his arm to help, the honoree waved him off. "Mr. President," he said smiling, "one does not need help going down, only going up."

This bittersweet quality pervaded the ceremony. Flanked by generals Schriever and LeMay, Cal Tech president Lee A. DuBridge, and Jerome Weisner, Kennedy spoke briefly, with Kármán at his side.

> I know of no one else who more completely represents all of the areas with which this award is appropriately concerned—science, engineering, and education. It is hard to visualize what the world would be like without aircraft and jet propulsion, or without the vision we have, just entering the realm of reality, of exploring space. I am especially glad to present this first National Medal of Science to one of the pioneers who has helped make all of this new and exciting age possible.[7]

With that, the president read the citation, citing Kármán's "leadership in the science and engineering basic to aeronautics, for distinguished counsel to armed services, and for promoting international co-operation in science and engineering." The Boss then took the lectern and declared himself "very, very much honored by this greatest distinction a scientist can get." He drew laughter recalling Hap Arnold's remark that his service in the Pentagon would "show the military that a college professor is good for something." Finally, with the medal in hand, he closed the proceedings with a warm, and at the same time, sad pledge: "What I can do in the rest of my life I do not know. But," he added, pointing to his head and smiling, "as far as I am in good health here, I will try to be grateful to this country." The gathering then adjourned to the National Academy of Sciences building where a luncheon honored the award winner. There, Lee DuBridge praised Kármán both for the imagination and the scope of his work, saying he was the rare individual who could have won the medal as easily for engineering as for pure science.[8]

Shortly after these festivities, Kármán boarded an aircraft for Paris, where he would spend the balance of the winter. His mood was good, and he continued to tend to AGARD business. But the Hungarian's health refused to mend and he decided, as he often had in the past, to visit the curative sulfur springs known to the Romans as Aquisgranum, to the Germans as the Elisenbrunnen spa of Aachen. The bustle of the city, restored since the war, would bring back happy memories and make him feel better. Before leaving Paris, he had lunch at a favorite Left Bank restaurant with some old friends: Ted Walkowicz, AGARD secretary June Merker, and Donald Putt's close associate Ralph Nunziato. Kármán prefaced the food in his traditional manner, with three double Manhattans (no water, three cherries each). They shared wine and enjoyed a happy meal. The three then led the Hungarian back to his hotel, even though he walked more steadily than they. When they parted, Walkowicz saw tears gathering in the old man's eyes. He could only guess the meaning.

Kármán left for Aachen on April 11 hoping the springs would strengthen him for the summer's travel. Between June and September he had scheduled no fewer than seven scientific meetings, ranging from Paris to Warsaw, Oslo to Athens, Washington to Pasadena, and then a return to Paris. In Aachen, he divided his time between soaking in the spa and visiting friends at the aeronautical institute he had made famous. But on the third of May a fit of coughing seized him as he floated in the baths. By the time he was pulled from the hot water, Kármán had suffered heart failure. Moved to the hospital, pneumonia set in and he gradually lost consciousness. Barbel Talbot, his dear companion of later years, sat vigil in his room. Finally, with her at his side, Theodore von Kármán succumbed in the early evening of Monday, May 6, 1963, only five days before his eighty-second birthday.[9]

As he had no next of kin, the U.S. Air Force, for whom he served as a consultant until his last day, arranged for removal of the body. Just hours after Kármán's death, Lt. Gen. James Ferguson, Air Staff deputy chief of staff for development, expressed the Service's "deepest sorrow and regret" at his passing. An hour after this cable, Air Force Vice-Chief of Staff Gen. William F. McKee sent a message to Systems Command's Gen. Bernard Schriever. Through Donald Putt, Schriever had developed close ties to Kármán and McKee asked him to summon an Air Force honor guard for the body's arrival in Los Angeles. Schriever made the arrangements, and on May 9 the dead man's remains were placed aboard a military air transport service aircraft in Rhein Main, Germany, and flown to Dover Air Force Base, Delaware. Frank Wattendorf accompanied the casket from Aachen to its final destination. The next day Kármán's body traveled aboard a commercial flight from Philadelphia to Los Angeles International Airport, where the promised honor guard snapped to attention at 11:20 A.M., just as the aircraft's wheels touched the tarmac. A hearse carried Kármán the long ride to 95 North Marengo Avenue, the address of the Turner and Stevens Funeral Home, Pasadena.

The executor of the estate, T. Edward Beehan, an Aerojet attorney and friend of the Boss's since the founding of the corporation, oversaw both the memorial and funeral services. On Tuesday, May 14, at 2 P.M., Beehan opened 1501 South Marengo Avenue for the last time. Once more, the living room, dining room, kitchen, and lawns teemed with his students, Cal Tech colleagues, scientists, and military men of high rank. So many attended, parked cars stretched half a mile in both directions from Kármán's gate. Marguerite Williams, his live-in secretary and housekeeper, stacked hundreds of telegrams and letters of condolence for the throngs to see. Air Force farewells poured in from Secretary of the Air Force Eugene Zuckert, Chief of Staff Gen. Curtis LeMay, Lt. Gen. James Ferguson, and Scientific Advisory Board chairman Guyford Stever. They all centered on Hap Arnold, *Toward New Horizons,* and the advisory board. Cal Tech president Lee DuBridge called him "one of the great men of his generation" and Dan Kimball, Aerojet Board chairman, declared expansively, "Our security . . . since Pearl Harbor has been based on the works of Einstein and Dr. von Kármán." Jet Propulsion Laboratory director William Pickering said, "His accomplishments were such as to dwarf the imagination." A brief service was performed in the home by the Reverend Arnold Biedermann, a Kármán admirer and pastor of St. Stephen's Roman Catholic Church in Los Angeles. The clergyman read a tribute from President Kennedy, who recalled his recent encounter with the Boss.

> It is with regret that I have learned of the death of Dr. Theodore von Kármán, to whom only last February I awarded the first National Medal of Science. Dr. von Kármán was known to the world's scientific community as the father of aerodynamics and as the chairman of the Aeronautical Research and Development Group to NATO which he organized ten years ago. I know that his friends and associates will mourn his loss and join me in paying tribute to a great scientist and humanitarian.[10]

The funeral cortege then snaked through Pasadena and Los Angeles to the Hollywood Memorial Cemetery on Santa Monica Boulevard. A rabbi officiated at a semi-private service in which select guests from the memorial, as well as others, participated. Reflecting the preferences of a lifetime, the group consisted of widely differing creeds, races, and nationalities. Impressive monuments to such movie celebrities as Douglas Fairbanks, Sr., Tyrone Power, and Cecil B. DeMille could be seen in the compact burial ground. But the Jewish section, where the group gathered, held the more modest and densely packed headstones of the less famous. Behind this segment spread a long, low building filled with simple crypts. Here, Helen and Josephine von Kármán had been laid to rest, one above the other, in a space the size of a tiny clothes closet. Now, next to them, at the bottom, lay Theodore von Kármán, as close to them in death as he had been in life.[11]

The way in which Theodore von Kármán arranged his final affairs tells much about his life. The day after the Rose Garden ceremony with President Kennedy, he visited Andrew Haley, still practicing law in Washington. Before leaving for Paris, the sick man wanted to draw a will. Here Haley learned his clients' abilities ranged beyond the purely scientific. Over the years, Kármán had invested wisely. His total wealth approached $475,000, no small fortune in 1963, considering his fine home and gardens were then valued at only $85,000. The bulk of Kármán's net worth derived from stock market holdings. He held shares in thirty-six firms, diversified among laboratories, energy companies, railways, and aerospace enterprises. The Boss's portfolio had an approximate value of $325,000.

Yet Kármán designated none of his money for self-perpetuation: no endowed chairs, no institutes, no fellowships, and no scientific prizes. He did leave $30,000 to the American-Hungarian Studies Foundation for translations of his father's work; $16,500 to the Research Fund of Art and Archaeology of the Spanish Institute in memory of Pipö; and his private papers, photographs, medals, and diplomas to the Guggenheim lab. But for the rest, Edward Beehan was empowered to "use his best discretion in disposing of the whole or any portion" of the remaining $425,000 in Kármán's estate. Cal Tech received the majority of the proceeds. Why did Kármán bother to draft a will less than three months before his death, yet designate the disposition of only 10 percent of his wealth?[12]

Two factors operated in his decision. First, the Boss disliked self-congratulation. He took great pleasure in tributes and awards, but these honors had to be earned honestly and bestowed legitimately. Second, he felt whatever fame he won should be based on *real* achievements, either as an institution-maker, a scientist, or a teacher. Hence, erecting memorials to himself only trivialized his accomplishments. Herein lay a lifelong contradiction: unassuming about his deeds, Kármán took delight when *others* recognized them. Clearly, he knew he was not an average person and had a high regard for his unusual abilities. On the other hand, he realized these qualities made him no better, in a humanistic sense, than other men and women. William Sears often observed these traits in the GALCIT days. "I think one reason why he charmed people," his student wrote, "was that he had a kind of humility. It was a special kind of humility . . . for he was a special person." Yet, to him, "being a great scientist or engineer was not really more important, in itself, than being a taxi driver or a bellhop." He enjoyed people because of their inner qualities, not because of their occupations. Many times Sears heard the Boss say, "I always assume the other fellow is exactly as smart as I." At the same time, when a bright student, full of admiration for the old professor, exclaimed, "Doctor, I will be happy if I can be only half as great as you," Kármán muttered out of earshot, "Now is that a modest ambition—.05?"[13]

Kármán's peculiar talent for liking and being liked stemmed from his father. Maurice von Kármán insisted upon a humane education for his gifted son. He also persuaded him to turn his mathematical inclination toward engineering, a field "nearer to everyday life." Theodore's consequent gift for human relations exerted a profound influence over his career. First, it lent itself to extraordinary teaching. Students never forgot the twisted handkerchiefs and the startlingly original equations, arrived at right before their eyes. They recalled evenings in his home and the youthful pleasures of being admitted to this worldly circle. They remembered his perpetual joy in discovery. In later years, when they themselves had achieved eminence in their native countries, in aeronautical industries, or in universities, Kármán's pupils acted upon these fond memories. Wherever he traveled, when members of the Kármán Circus learned his itinerary, they gathered at train stations and air terminals. Onlookers watched in surprise as bunches of scientists surrounded the old man, a sight as likely to occur in Tokyo or Bombay as in Kansas City or Seattle. Moreover, his students—and the students of his students—memorialized him in their work. During the quarter century after his death, no fewer than fifty-seven American doctoral dissertations treated problems in physics, aerodynamics, and mathematics which were *direct* outgrowths of his scholarship.[14]

The Kármán élan likewise influenced his effectiveness as an institution-builder. It persuaded colleagues to regard him as a benign presence, above the usual bureaucratic in-fighting, a kindly professor who simply wished to pursue scientific study. The reality conflicted with the appearance. Pupils at GALCIT who thought Kármán's title of director merely honorary soon learned that Clark Millikan did nothing substantive without the Boss's knowledge. Kármán chose assistants of high scientific and administrative caliber and allowed them the dignity of appearing to run affairs. But "in all vital areas he knew exactly what went on and why . . . He carried the salary budget, including laboratory assistants and post doctorates, item by item, in his head." When an older Ph.D. candidate with practical experience in aircraft design sought admittance to the Cal Tech aeronautics department, the Hungarian asked the faculty whether the man should be compelled to take all of the required courses. Everyone said he should. "I am Director," said Kármán, "and I vote No. So [he] does not have to take the courses. That is academic democracy." Such cases reveal the basis of his organizational genius. His "ready wit and ability to point out absurdity and inconsistency in an argument without hurting the feelings of the man who produced it" kept colleagues on track, soothed tempers, and affected compromise.[15]

Theodore von Kármán's science also reflected this humanistic orientation. He did not seek to broaden knowledge just for its own sake; rather, he sought scientific answers to the basic problems of flight. "There is nothing more practical," he would tell his engineer friends, "than a good theory." Moreover, his solutions were strongly *intuitive,* often founded on sudden bursts of insight about the fundamental nature of physical events. These flashes led Kármán to the underlying mechanics of fluid motion, which he achieved through highly transparent mathematical approximations. With these equations in hand, he and his associates switched on the wind tunnel and, through experimentation, pressed the mathematical descriptions to their limits. In short, the Boss viewed science the same way as his father: a branch of knowledge practiced not as a trade but as an art.[16]

Through this process, Kármán helped lower the barriers between engineering and science. In the past, engineers resorted to empiricism and time-honored formulae out of frustration with theorems that failed in practice. The Hungarian devoted his scholarly career to delving into the underlying laws of physics and mathematics to serve the specific needs of aerodynamic design. As a consequence, modern, science-based engineering emerged first in aeronautics and spread outward to other fields. Kármán broke down these walls through scientific insight. His deeds also reflect a highly integrated view of life. He not only sought to remove the barricades dividing the engineer from the scientist, but personified a free flow among work and leisure, art and science, students and teachers, home and classroom, thinkers and laborers, military men and "long hairs." Theodore von Kármán's legacy stems from fluid motion—the kind he imagined in equations, and the kind he experienced in life.[17]

# Notes

## ABBREVIATIONS

| | |
|---|---|
| AFHRC | U.S. Air Force Historical Research Center Archives |
| AFSC/HO | Headquarters Air Force Systems Command History Office files (available at the Headquarters Air Force Materiel Command History Office, Dayton, Ohio) |
| AGARD | (NATO) Advisory Group for Aeronautical Research and Development |
| GALCIT | Guggenheim Aeronautical Laboratory, California Institute of Technology |
| ICBM | Intercontinental ballistic missile |
| JATO | Jet-assisted takeoff |
| JPL | Jet Propulsion Laboratory |
| NACA | National Advisory Committee for Aeronautics |
| NAS | National Academy of Sciences Archives |
| NATO | North Atlantic Treaty Organization |
| NYU | New York University |
| OAFH | Office of Air Force History, Washington, D.C. |
| ORDCIT | Ordnance, California Institute of Technology |
| R&D | Research and development |
| SAB | Scientific Advisory Board |
| TVK | Theodore von Kármán Collection at the California Institute of Technology, Microfiche Edition |
| USAFA | U.S. Air Force Academy Archives |

## CHAPTER 1. HIS FATHER'S SON

1. Several of Kármán's students recollect in published sources on the parties at South Marengo. See William R. Sears, "Some Recollections of Theodore von Kármán," in *Theodore von Kármán, 1881–1963, In Memoriam* (Philadelphia: Printed by the Society for Industrial and Applied Mathematics, 1965), 4–5 (hereafter "Some Recollections"); W. D. Rannie, "Dr. Theodore von Kármán: His Achievements Live Forever," *Western Aerospace* (June 1963): ii

(hereafter Rannie, "Kármán"); W. D. Rannie, "Theodore von Kármán, 1881–1963," *Engineering and Science* (June 1963): 17 (hereafter Rannie, "Theodore von Kármán"); Clark B. Millikan, "Theodore von Kármán—His American Period," *Journal of the Royal Aeronautical Society* (1963): 617; E. E. Sechler, "A Salute to Todor," *Engineering and Science* (May 1956): 8.

Important details on Kármán's home life are also available in his autobiography (with Lee Edson), *The Wind and Beyond: Theodore von Kármán, Pioneer in Aviation and Pathfinder in Space* (Boston: Little, Brown, 1967), 6, 8, 12. *The Wind and Beyond* is invaluable to understanding Theodore von Kármán and to reconstructing his life. But like autobiographies of most famous figures, its use requires much caution. On occasions, its sequence of events differs significantly from other sources. Edson is appropriately generous with Kármán's successes, but sometimes attributes more to him than is warranted. Some of the contextual material is incorrect. Even more questionable is the method by which the book was produced. Fearing its completion lest it hasten his death, Kármán expired when the text was only three-fourths finished. Until this point, Edson had conducted interviews with the Boss over a number of years. After each session, he drafted a first-person narrative and submitted it to Kármán for review. "It is me in good English," the scientist quipped. The last quarter Edson wrote himself. Considering, too, the variety of sources Edson evidently brought to bear (but did not reference), *The Wind and Beyond* is not really biography or autobiography, but a patchwork of the two.

Finally, the oral record fills in some of the story, for instance: interview between Shirley Thomas and M. Gorn, Los Angeles, December 30, 1989; interview between Dr. William Pickering and M. Gorn, Pasadena, December 27, 1989; interview between Prof. William Sears and M. Gorn, Tucson, February 6, 1990. The Thomas and Sears interviews were conducted by telephone.

2. S. Goldstein, "Theodore von Kármán, 1881–1963," in *Biographical Memoirs of the Fellows of the Royal Society* (1966): 335; Kármán, *Wind and Beyond,* 15, 20, 27; R. Cargill Hall, "Shaping the Course of Aeronautics, Rocketry, and Astronautics: Theodore von Kármán, 1881–1963," *Journal of the Astronautical Sciences* (Oct.–Dec. 1978): 369–70. Mr. Hall has written two other pieces on Theodore von Kármán: one was read on October 9, 1976, at the symposium of the International Space Hall of Fame–International Academy of Astronautics; the other is in *Aerospace Historian* (Dec. 1981): 253–58, published in honor of Kármán's 100th anniversary. The work in *Astronautical Sciences* is the most comprehensive of the three and is the only one cited in this book.

3. Kármán, *Wind and Beyond,* 15, 16, 18–20; "Obituaries," *Physics Today* (July 1963): 74; Goldstein, "Kármán," 335; Frank L. Wattendorf and Frank J. Malina, "Theodore von Kármán, 1881–1963," *Astronautica Acta* (1964): 81 (hereafter Wattendorf and Malina, "Kármán").

4. Kármán, *Wind and Beyond,* 16–19; Hall, "Shaping Aeronautics," 370; Wattendorf and Malina, "Kármán," 82.

5. Kármán, *Wind and Beyond,* 16, 19–20; Hall, "Shaping Aeronautics," 371; Wattendorf and Malina, "Kármán," 82.

6. Kármán, *Wind and Beyond,* 18–19.

7. Interview, Theodore von Kármán with Shirley Thomas, Pasadena, January 12, 1960. An audiotape of the interview is available at the Eli Lilly Library, University of Indiana–Bloomington. See also Kármán, *Wind and Beyond,* 15–16; Hall, "Shaping Aeronautics," 371; Wattendorf and Malina, "Kármán," 82; Lee Edson, "He Tamed the Wind," *Saturday Evening Post* (August 3, 1957), 77; Shirley Thomas, *Men of Space,* 8 vols. (Philadelphia: Chilton, 1960–68), 1:160. One true biography of Kármán does exist: Daniel S. Halacy, Jr., *Father of Supersonic Flight: Theodore von Kármán* (New York: Julian Messner, 1965). On pages 9–14, Halacy describes in detail young Todor's mathematical "tricks" and his father's reaction. This incident and some others in the book reduce its credibility, quoting long conversations without reference to sources. In fact, the book has neither notes nor bibliography. Written for young adults, *Father of Supersonic Flight* does, nonetheless, seem to have the basic facts right, and if used with care, offers some useful information on Kármán's life.

8. In the interview with Shirley Thomas, Kármán related a story about John von Neumann, the brilliant Hungarian mathematician. It might have been a parable for Kármán's own paternal relations. Von Neumann's father was a prosperous banker and opposed his son pursuing mathematics, a subject in which the boy displayed brilliance. He brought the young man to Kármán to dissuade him from following this inclination. Kármán affected a compromise: the junior von Neumann would study chemical engineering. But his true calling could not be denied; he took a doctorate in mathematics and eventually discovered the conceptual key to the modern computer. "You can't change [a person's nature]," Kármán wryly observed. The other sources cited above in n. 7 apply also to this note.

9. Interview, Kármán with Thomas; Thomas, *Men of Space* 1:160–61; Wattendorf and Malina, "Kármán," 82.

10. Kármán, *Wind and Beyond,* 23; Hall, "Shaping Aeronautics," 371; Thomas, *Men of Space* 1:160.

11. Carlile Aylmer Macartney, *Hungary, A Short History* (Edinburgh: Edinburgh University Press, 1962), 122–207; Paul Ignotus, *Hungary* (New York: Praeger, 1972), 57–106.

12. Kármán, *Wind and Beyond,* 20–25; Halacy, *Supersonic Flight,* 15; Wattendorf and Malina, "Kármán," 82.

13. Kármán, *Wind and Beyond,* 22–23, 25.

14. Wattendorf and Malina, "Kármán," 82; Kármán, *Wind and Beyond,* 25–26.

15. Kármán, *Wind and Beyond,* 26–31; Wattendorf and Malina, "Kármán," 82; G. I. Taylor, "Memories of Kármán," *Journal of Fluid Mechanics* (1963): 478; Hugh L. Dryden, "Theodore von Kármán," *Yearbook of the Amer ican Philosophical Society* (1963): 159–60 (hereafter Dryden, "Kármán"); Hugh L. Dryden, "The Contributions of Theodore von Kármán: A Review," *Astronautics and Aerospace Engineering* (July 1963): 12 (hereafter "Contributions").

16. Older brothers Elemer and Feri had by now established themselves as teachers. Miklos became a banker. Halacy, *Supersonic Flight,* 15; Kármán, *Wind and Beyond,* 31.

17. Millikan, "Kármán—His American Period," 615; Kármán, *Wind and Beyond,* 31–32; Halacy, *Supersonic Flight,* 16.

18. Interview, Kármán with Thomas; Kármán, *Wind and Beyond,* 32–33; Dryden, "Contributions," 12; Hugh L. Dryden, "Theodore von Kármán, 1881–1963," *Biographical Memoirs of the National Academy of Sciences* (1965): 346–47 (hereafter "Theodore von Kármán"); Dryden, "Kármán," 160; Hugh L. Dryden, "Contributions of Theodore von Kármán to Applied Mechanics," *Applied Mechanics Review* (August 1963): 590 (hereafter "Contributions of Theodore von Kármán").

19. Kármán, *Wind and Beyond,* 33–34; Halacy, *Supersonic Flight,* 18; Dryden, "Theodore von Kármán," 347; Wattendorf and Malina, "Kármán," 83; Goldstein, "Kármán," 336.

## CHAPTER 2. SCIENTIST AND SOLDIER

1. Paul A. Hanle, *Bringing Aerodynamics to America* (Cambridge: MIT Press, 1982), 23–33; Kármán, *Wind and Beyond,* 34 (see chap. 1, n. 1). Isaak Moiseevich Yaglom, *Felix Klein and Sophus Lie: Evolution of the Idea of Symmetry in the Nineteenth Century* (Boston: Birkhauser, 1988), reviewed in *Physics Today* (June 1989): 73–74, by Luis Alvarez-Gaumé.

2. Kármán, *Wind and Beyond,* 35.

3. Thomas, *Men of Space* 1:162 (see chap. 1, n. 7); Kármán, *Wind and Beyond,* 35–41; Dryden, "Contributions," 12 (see chap. 1, n. 15); Dryden, "Theodore von Kármán," 347–48 (see chap. 1, n. 18).

4. Wattendorf and Malina, "Kármán," 83 (see chap. 1, n. 3); Kármán, *Wind and Beyond,* 41–42; *The New Encyclopedia Brittanica (Micropaedia),* 15th ed., s.v. "Theodore von Kármán" by Frank J. Malina, 746 (hereafter Malina, "Theodore von Kármán"); Halacy, *Supersonic Flight,* 19–24 (see chap. 1, n. 7); Tom D. Crouch, "Taking to the Air: Modern Aviation Got Its Lift from Vacuum Cleaners and Vortices," *Science* (November 1984): 79–82.

5. Kármán, *Wind and Beyond,* 42–44; Halacy, *Supersonic Flight,* 24–33; Crouch, "Taking to the Air," 79–82; Wattendorf and Malina, "Kármán," 83–84; Malina, "Theodore von Kármán," 746.

6. Hanle, *Bringing Aerodynamics,* 42–49; "L. Prandtl: A Tribute in Honor of His 75th Birthday," *Mechanical Engineering* (February 1950): 116.

7. Theodore von Kármán, *Collected Works of Theodore von Kármán,* 4 vols. (1902–13) (London: Butterworth, 1956), 1:53–61. Reprint of an article that first appeared in the *Journal of the Society of Hungarian Engineers and Architects* (1908).

8. Kármán, *Wind and Beyond,* 44–47; Halacy, *Supersonic Flight,* 36–37; Thomas, *Men of Space* 1:162–63.

9. Kármán, *Wind and Beyond,* 56.

10. Kármán, *Wind and Beyond,* 44–47; Halacy, *Supersonic Flight,* 37–40. For a more technical description of the origins of flight science, see Theodore von Kármán, *Aerodynamics: Selected Topics in Light of Their Historical Development* (Ithaca, N.Y.: Cornell University Press, 1954), 1–67.

11. Kármán, *Aerodynamics,* 70; Kármán, *Wind and Beyond,* 62; Halacy, *Supersonic Flight,* 40–44.

12. Kármán, *Wind and Beyond,* 63; interview, Kármán with Thomas, January 12, 1960; Kármán, *Aerodynamics,* 70–71.

13. Kármán, *Aerodynamics,* 71.

14. Hanle, *Bringing Aerodynamics,* 54–61; Kármán, *Wind and Beyond,* 63–65; Kármán, *Aerodynamics,* 71–73; Halacy, *Supersonic Flight,* 44–45.

15. Kármán, *Wind and Beyond,* 65–71; Dryden, "Theodore von Kármán," 349.

16. Kármán, *Wind and Beyond,* 71–73; Dryden, "Theodore von Kármán," 349; Wattendorf and Malina, "Kármán," 84.

17. Kármán, *Wind and Beyond,* 74.

18. Wattendorf and Malina, *Kármán,* 87; Dryden, "Contributions of Theodore von Kármán," 590 (see chap. 1, n. 18); Dryden, "Theodore von Kármán," 349; Kármán, *Wind and Beyond,* 73–75; Hanle, *Bringing Aerodynamics,* 61–62.

19. Hanle, *Bringing Aerodynamics,* 62–67; "L. Prandtl," 116; Crouch, "Taking to the Air," 79–81.

20. Julius C. Rotta, "The Prandtl Hergesell Project of a National Research Establishment for Aeronautics," European Space Agency Technical Translation No. 835, June 1984, pp. 3, 46–61; Wattendorf and Malina, "Kármán," 84.

21. Kármán, *Wind and Beyond,* 75–78; Hanle, *Bringing Aerodynamics,* 62; Halacy, *Supersonic Flight,* 48–51; Dryden, "Contributions of Theodore von Kármán," 590.

22. Taylor, "Memories of Kármán," 478–79 (see chap. 1, n. 15).

23. Kármán, *Wind and Beyond,* 78–79; Halacy, *Supersonic Flight,* 51–54.

24. Dryden, "Contributions," 12–13; Kármán, *Wind and Beyond,* 80; Halacy, *Supersonic Flight;* 54–55; Dryden; "Contributions of Theodore von Kármán," 590; Hanle, *Bringing Aerodynamics,* 62.

25. Kármán, *Wind and Beyond,* 80–89; Halacy, *Supersonic Flight,* 55–61; Dryden, "Contributions," 12; Goldstein, "Kármán," 339 (see chap. 1, n. 2); Hanle, *Bringing Aerodynamics,* 62.

26. Kármán, *Wind and Beyond,* 82, 89–95; Thomas, *Men of Space* 1:165; Halacy, *Supersonic Flight,* 61–62.

27. Kármán, *Wind and Beyond,* 96–97, 103–4, 107; Halacy, *Supersonic Flight,* 63; Hall, "Shaping Aeronautics," 374 (see chap. 1, n. 2); Dryden, "Theodore von Kármán," 360.

## CHAPTER 3. FROM AACHEN TO PASADENA

1. Kármán, *Wind and Beyond,* 96–97, 103–4, 107 (see chap. 1, n. 1); Halacy, *Supersonic Flight,* 63 (see chap. 1, n. 7); Hall, "Shaping Aeronautics," 374 (see chap. 1, n. 2); Dryden, "Theodore von Kármán," 360 (see chap. 1, n. 18).

2. Hanle, *Bringing Aerodynamics,* 62–63 (see chap. 2, n. 1); Dryden, "Theodore von Kármán," 350.

3. Kármán, *Aerodynamics,* 89 (see chap. 2, n. 10); Dryden, "Contributions of Theodore von Kármán," 591 (see chap. 1, n. 18).

4. Millikan, "Kármán—His American Period," 615 (see chap. 1, n. 1); Malina, "Theodore von Kármán," 746 (see chap. 2, n. 4); Goldstein, "Kármán," 339 (see chap. 1, n. 2); Dryden, "Kármán," 161 (see chap. 1, n. 15); Hall, "Shaping Aeronautics," 374; Dryden, "Theodore von Kármán," 350; Halacy, *Supersonic Flight,* 63–64; Kármán, *Wind and Beyond,* 105–8; see also Edson, "He Tamed the Wind," 78 (see chap. 1, n. 7); interview, Kármán with Thomas, January 12, 1960.

5. Interview, Kármán with Thomas.

6. Kármán, *Wind and Beyond,* 105; interview, Kármán with Thomas.

7. Kármán, *Wind and Beyond,* 106.

8. Ibid., 106–9; Edson, "He Tamed the Wind," 78; interview, Kármán with Thomas.

9. Kármán, *Wind and Beyond,* 104–5; Malina, "Theodore von Kármán," 746; Hanle, *Bringing Aerodynamics,* 63; Goldstein, "Kármán," 339.

10. Dryden, "Contributions of Theodore von Kármán," 591; Hanle, *Bringing Aerodynamics,* 63.

11. Dryden, "Contributions of Theodore von Kármán," 591; Hanle, *Bringing Aerodynamics,* 63; Kármán, *Wind and Beyond,* 105.

12. Kármán, *Wind and Beyond,* 110–19; Dryden, "Contributions of Theodore von Kármán," 591; Hanle, *Bringing Aerodynamics,* 63–64.

13. Hanle, *Bringing Aerodynamics,* 64–67.

14. For this material I owe a large debt to Paul Hanle's excellent book, *Bringing Aerodynamics to America*. Hanle, *Bringing Aerodynamics,* 80–92; Alex Roland, "The Impact of War upon Aeronautical Progress: The Experience of the NACA," in *Air Power and Warfare: Proceedings of the 8th Military History Symposium,* U.S. Air Force Academy, October 18–20, 1978, ed. Alfred F. Hurley and Robert C. Ehrhart (Washington, D.C.: Office of Air Force History and the U.S. Air Force Academy, 1979), 367–71.

15. *The Guggenheim Aeronautical Laboratory of the California Institute of Technology (GALCIT): The First Twenty-five Years* (Pasadena: Cal Tech, 1954), 5–6 (hereafter *GALCIT: The First Twenty-five Years*).

16. William R. Sears and Mabel R. Sears, "The Kármán Years at GALCIT," *Annual Review of Fluid Mechanics* (1978): 1–2; Dryden, "Theodore von Kármán," 351; Kármán, *Wind and Beyond,* 120; interview, Kármán with Thomas.

17. Richard P. Hallion, *Legacy of Flight: The Guggenheim Contribution to American Aviation* (Seattle: University of Washington Press, 1977), 20–33.

18. Interview, Kármán with Thomas.

19. Ibid.

20. "The Triple Alliance: Millikan, Guggenheim, and von Kármán," *Engineering and Science* [Cal Tech] (April 1981): 24; Kármán, *Wind and Beyond,* 121–22; interview, Kármán with Thomas; interview, Harry Guggenheim with Donald Shaughnessy, April 6, 1960, Air Force Historical Research Center archives (hereafter abbreviated as AFHRC); Hallion, *Legacy,* 46–48.

21. Hanle, *Bringing Aerodynamics,* 93–97; "Triple Alliance," 24–25; Hallion, *Legacy,* 50.

22. Hanle, *Bringing Aerodynamics,* 98–101; Hallion, *Legacy,* 51–52; Kármán, *Wind and Beyond,* 120–21; "Triple Alliance," 26.

23. Interview, Guggenheim with Shaughnessy; Thomas, *Men of Space,* 1:166–67 (see chap. 1, n. 7); Hallion, *Legacy,* 52; Kármán, *Wind and Beyond,* 121–23.

24. *Bulletin of the California Institute of Technology: New Courses in Aeronautics* (Pasadena: Cal Tech, 1926) 1–17; Kármán, *Wind and Beyond,* 124–26; Sears and Sears, "GALCIT," 2–3; Halacy, *Supersonic Flight,* 76–77; *GALCIT: The First Twenty-five Years,* 6.

25. Hanle, *Bringing Aerodynamics,* 102; "Triple Alliance," 26.

26. Kármán, *Wind and Beyond,* 127, 128, 145.

27. Hanle, *Bringing Aerodynamics,* 101–2; Thomas, *Men of Space,* 1:167; Kármán, *Wind and Beyond,* 128; Hallion, *Legacy,* 52–53; "Triple Alliance," 26; Sears and Sears, "GALCIT," 3.

28. Kármán, *Wind and Beyond,* 129–33.

29. *Bulletin of the California Institute of Technology Annual Catalogue* (Pasadena: Cal Tech, 1927), 56–57; *Bulletin of the California Institute of Technology*

*Annual Catalogue* (Pasadena: Cal Tech, 1929), 58; *GALCIT: The First Twenty-five Years*, 7.

30. Kármán, *Wind and Beyond*, 140–41. *Cal Tech Bulletin: The Daniel Guggenheim Graduate School of Aeronautics of the California Institute of Technology: A History of its First Ten Years* (Pasadena: Cal Tech, 1940), 5 (hereafter *GALCIT: The First Ten Years*); Hanle, *Bringing Aerodynamics*, 123–24.

31. I am indebted to Hanle, *Bringing Aerodynamics*, 104–22, for this discussion of Kármán's troubles with German academia.

32. Hanle, *Bringing Aerodynamics*, 124–26; Kármán, *Wind and Beyond*, 141–42.

33. Kármán, *Wind and Beyond*, 142, 145; Thomas, *Men of Science*, 1:168; Goldstein, "Kármán," 341.

34. Hanle, *Bringing Aerodynamics*, 124–25.

35. Ibid., 124–27, 129–30; Hallion, *Legacy*, 67–69.

36. Hanle, *Bringing Aerodynamics*, 127–35; Kármán, *Wind and Beyond*, 145–46; "Triple Alliance," 26.

## CHAPTER 4. A MAGNET FOR AERONAUTICS

1. According to Stanley Brozek, the present owner of Kármán's residence, Cal Tech held 1501 South Marengo Avenue until the early 1970s, when it was sold after neighbors rebuffed attempts to convert it to administrative offices. It was then purchased by Brozek. I wish to thank him for kindly allowing me to walk the grounds and tour the inside of his home in December 1989. During my visit, he also informed me that the home was vacant during Cal Tech's ownership. With the exception of a small swimming pool, a retaining wall at the rear of the house, and a few gardening touches added by Brozek, the property is virtually unchanged since the day Kármán left in February 1963. A description of its furnishings and the exact location of the lot may be found in Theodore von Kármán's will (#NEP-3517) in a listing entitled "Inventory and Appraisement," on file at the Pasadena courthouse; interview, Sears with Gorn, February 6, 1990.

2. Hanle, *Bringing Aerodynamics*, 131, 133–34 (see chap. 2, n. 1); Kármán, *Wind and Beyond*, 145–46 (see chap. 1, n. 1); Thomas, *Men of Space*, 1:169 (see chap. 1, n. 7).

3. Kármán, *Wind and Beyond*, 147; *Bulletin of the California Institute of Technology: Announcement of the Graduate School of Aeronautics* (Pasadena: Cal Tech, 1930); *GALCIT: The First Twenty-five Years*, 7 (see chap. 3, n. 15).

4. *GALCIT: The First Ten Years*, 7–8, 15–17, 22–23 (see chap. 3, n. 30); interview, Sears with Gorn; *GALCIT: The First Twenty-five Years*, 20–24, 28.

5. Not everyone approved of GALCIT. Indeed, the NACA leadership regarded the Cal Tech lab as a claimant to its aeronautical supremacy.

When George Lewis, the director of NACA, learned of the remarkable efficiency of the new Pasadena wind tunnel, he dispatched his top aerodynamics scientist, Eastman Jacobs, to study the machine. Lewis also answered the GALCIT challenge by proposing a modern, government-sponsored laboratory in Sunnyvale, California. He hoped such an establishment would check Kármán's dominance over flight science in the western United States. Lewis was so fixed on this policy that all through the 1930s he pressed Congress to appropriate funds. His lobbying finally resulted in the opening of the Ames Aeronautical Laboratory at Moffett Field, some ten years after his rival settled permanently in Los Angeles.

Failing to knock GALCIT out with a quick blow, the NACA chief attempted to bully the Hungarian into submission. Cal Tech, said Lewis, should pursue just one objective: to prepare young scientists for careers in NACA, the only *national* aeronautics organization capable of building first-class research centers and wind tunnels. "I couldn't disagree more," wrote the energetic and ambitious Kármán. Why *not* fashion GALCIT into a regional powerhouse of industrial and military research and consulting?

Ultimately, George Lewis's worst fears were realized. Through his personal ties with Gen. Henry "Hap" Arnold, Kármán undertook extensive consultations with the Army Air Forces and formed a permanent board of scientific experts. Once U.S. airpower leaders followed his advice and erected their own research infrastructure, NACA became all but irrelevant to American military aviation. Alex Roland, *Model Research: The National Advisory Committee for Aeronautics, 1915–1958,* 2 vols. (Washington, D.C.: NASA, 1985), 1:158–75, 217; Kármán, *Wind and Beyond,* 126, 168–72, 226; Theodore von Kármán and Clark B. Millikan, "The Use of the Wind Tunnel in Connection with Aircraft Design Problems," *Transactions of the American Society of Mechanical Engineers* (1934): 151; interview, Prof. Homer J. Stewart with Gorn, Altadena, California, December 29, 1989 (by telephone).

6. Hallion, *Legacy,* 69 (see chap. 3, n. 17); Kármán, *Wind and Beyond,* 160–61; Preface and Introduction, *The Daniel Guggenheim Airship Institute Publication No. 1* (Akron, Ohio: The Institute, 1933), v, 7–10.

7. Kármán, *Wind and Beyond,* 160–67; Theodore von Kármán, "Some Aerodynamic Problems in Airships," *Guggenheim Airship Institute Publication No. 1* (Akron, Ohio: The Institute, 1933), 45–46; Theodore von Kármán, "Introduction," in the *Guggenheim Airship Institute Publication No. 2* (Akron, Ohio: The Institute, 1935), iii–iv; Wattendorf and Malina, "Kármán," 84 (see chap. 1, n. 3).

8. Interview, Kármán with Thomas, January 12, 1960.

9. Theodore von Kármán, "Turbulence" (Twenty-fifth Wilbur Wright Memorial Lecture), *Journal of the Royal Aeronautical Society* (1937): 1109, 1111; Kármán, *Wind and Beyond,* 134; interview, Kármán with Thomas.

10. Kármán, *Wind and Beyond,* 134–35; Kármán, "Turbulence," 1111.

11. Dryden, "Theodore von Kármán," 352–53 (see chap. 1, n. 18); Kármán, *Wind and Beyond,* 136–37.

12. Kármán, *Wind and Beyond,* 137, 139; Dryden, "Theodore von Kármán," 352; Dryden, "Contributions of Theodore von Kármán," 592 (see chap. 1, n. 18); Kármán, *Aerodynamics,* 92–93 (see chap. 2, n. 10).

13. Kármán, *Wind and Beyond,* 137–40.

14. Ibid., 138–39; Dryden, "Contributions of Theodore von Kármán," 592.

15. The interior of Kármán's home is drawn from the author's visit with its present owners in December 1989 (see chap. 4, n. 1) and from Kármán's will, "Inventory and Appraisement," 4–16; from Kármán, *Wind and Beyond,* 6, 9; and from interview, Thomas with Gorn, December 30, 1989. See also "Dr. Theodore von Kármán: Biographical Sketch," U.S. Air Force Academy Archives (hereafter USAFA).

16. Kármán, *Wind and Beyond,* 11–12; Rannie, "Theodore von Kármán," 17 (see chap. 1, n. 1); Sears, "Some Recollections," 4–5 (see chap. 1, n. 1); interview, Thomas with Gorn; Clark B. Millikan, "Kármán—An Appreciation," in *Theodore von Kármán Anniversary Volume* (Pasadena: Cal Tech, 1941), ix; Goldstein, "Kármán," 34 (see chap. 1, n. 2); interview, Sears with Gorn; interview, Pickering with Gorn, December 27, 1989; interview, Stewart with Gorn; interview, Kármán with Thomas; Edson, "He Tamed the Wind," 76–77 (see chap. 1, n. 7).

17. Koko meant so much to Kármán that he commissioned an artist to paint him in oils. The painting was on the wall of his study the day the Boss died. Yet, the dog had practical, as well as sentimental, value; it protected his mother and sister during Kármán's many domestic and foreign travels. Kármán, *Wind and Beyond,* 6; Kármán's will, "Inventory and Appraisement," 9; interview, Prof. John A. Schutz with Prof. Hallett Smith, Los Angeles, February 22, 1990.

18. Interview, Kármán with Thomas; Rannie, "Theodore von Kármán," 17; interview, Sears with Gorn; Sechler, "A Salute to Todor," 8 (see chap. 1, n. 1).

19. Goldstein, "Kármán," 345; Edson, "He Tamed the Wind," 78 (see chap. 1, n. 7); Rannie, "Theodore von Kármán," 17; Hugh L. Dryden, "The Contributions of Theodore von Kármán to Science and Technology," in *Collected Works of Theodore von Kármán* (see chap. 2, n. 7), 1:ix (hereafter "Kármán to Science"); Halacy, *Supersonic Flight,* 104 (see chap. 1, n. 7).

20. Sears, "Some Recollections," 2, 4–5; Rannie, "Kármán," 11 (see chap. 1, n. 1); interview, Sears with Gorn; Kármán, *Wind and Beyond,* 12; Kár-

mán's will, "Inventory and Appraisement," 9–10; Edson, "He Tamed the Wind," 22.

21. Interview, Sears with Gorn; Sears and Sears, "GALCIT," 3–4 (see chap. 3, n. 16); interview, Dorothy Lewis (GALCIT secretary, 1942–46) with James H. Wilson, June 15, 1972, Jet Propulsion Laboratory Archives (hereafter abbreviated as JPL).

22. Sears, "Some Recollections," 3–4; Kármán, *Wind and Beyond,* 8.

23. Interview, Sears with Gorn; Sears and Sears, "GALCIT," 8–9; Sears, "Some Recollections," 3; Rannie, "Kármán," 11; Millikan, "Kármán—His American Period," 615 (see chap. 1, n. 1); Kármán, *Wind and Beyond,* 8–9.

24. Interview, Kármán with Thomas; Kármán, *Wind and Beyond,* 148–49.

25. Interview, Sears with Gorn; Sears and Sears, "GALCIT," 5; Wattendorf and Malina, "Kármán," 84; Dryden, "Kármán to Science," 1:viii; *American Men and Women of Science* (Physical and Biological Sciences), 14th ed., 1979, entries under William R. Sears, Homer J. Stewart, Frank Marble, Ernest Sechler, and Frank J. Malina.

## CHAPTER 5. THE ROCKETEERS

1. Interview, Stewart with Gorn, December 29, 1989.

2. N. A. Rynin, *Interplanetary Flight and Communication* 3, no. 8, *Theory of Space Flight* (translated from Russian) (Jerusalem: Israel Program for Scientific Translations, 1976), 98, 135; Theodore von Kármán and Frank J. Malina, "Beginnings of Astronautics," in Theodore von Kármán, *The Collected Works of Theodore von Kármán, 1952–1963,* ed. G. Gabrielli et al. (Rhode St. Genèse, Belgium: Von Kármán Institute for Fluid Dynamics, 1975), pt. 2, 348–64.

3. Theodore von Kármán, "Jet Assisted Take-off," *Interavia* (July 1952): 377 (hereafter "JATO"); Kármán, *Wind and Beyond,* 236–37 (see chap. 1, n. 1); Kármán and Malina, "Astronautics," 7; Goldstein, "Kármán," 341 (see chap. 1, n. 2).

4. Interview, Dr. Frank J. Malina with R. Cargill Hall, October 29, 1968, JPL; Kármán, *Wind and Beyond,* 235, 238; Frank J. Malina, "Memoir on the GALCIT Rocket Research Project, 1936–1938," June 6, 1967, 1–3, JPL (prepared for the First International Symposium on the History of Astronautics, "Pre-1939 Memoirs of Astronautics," organized by the International Academy of Astronautics in cooperation with the International Union of the History and Philosophy of Science, Belgrade, September 25–26, 1967); Clayton R. Koppes, *JPL and the American Space Program: A History of the Jet Propulsion Laboratory* (New Haven: Yale University Press, 1982), 2–3; Kármán and Malina, "Astronautics," 8.

5. Kármán, *Wind and Beyond,* 235; Frank J. Malina, "Rocket Research and Development: Excerpts from Letters Written Home by Frank J. Malina between 1936 and 1946," JPL, p. 2; Malina, "Memoir on GALCIT Rocket Research," 3–4.

6. Malina, "Memoir on GALCIT Rocket Research," 3–5; Kármán, *Wind and Beyond,* 235, 238–39; Malina, "Rocket Research and Development," 2–3.

7. Kármán, *Wind and Beyond,* 241–42; Malina, "Memoir on GALCIT Rocket Research," 6–8; Koppes, *JPL and the American Space Program,* 4; Halacy, *Supersonic Flight,* 111–12 (see chap. 1, n. 7); Milton Lehman, *Robert H. Goddard: Pioneer of Space Research* (rpt.: New York: Da Capo Press, 1988), 234–35 (a reprint of Lehman's 1963 book *The High Man: Robert H. Goddard*); interview, Theodore von Kármán with Donald Shaughnessy, January 27, 1960, AFHRC.

8. Interview, Malina with Hall; Millikan, "Kármán—His American Period," 616 (see chap. 1, n. 1); Malina, "Rocket Research and Development," 3–4; Malina, "Memoir on Rocket Research," 10–11.

9. Kármán treated Tsien like the rest of his students. Once they graduated, he retained close ties, helping them obtain positions and research funding whenever possible. But in this case, his patronage proved insufficient to prevent tragic events. From his first encounter with Tsien in 1936, the Hungarian knew the Peking native had a special brillance and invited him to do advanced studies at GALCIT. With Kármán's backing, he received a full professorship at MIT in 1947. Two years later, he returned to Cal Tech to direct the newly established Daniel and Florence Guggenheim Jet Propulsion Center.

Unfortunately, Sen. Joseph R. McCarthy's hearings on Communist infiltration of American institutions placed men like Tsien under suspicion. Not only had he been born in China, which had just joined the growing ranks of Communist nations, but Tsien had worked for years on classified rocket projects. The American Communist hunters assumed Chinese and Soviet scientists lacked the wherewithal to develop rocketry, missiles, and atomic weapons themselves; their successes must be the result of espionage.

In any event, Tsien aroused the interest of the Federal Bureau of Investigation when he refused to testify in a perjury case involving a colleague with alleged Communist sympathies. As a result, in July 1950 Tsien's security clearance was revoked. Bitter and angry, he turned to Cal Tech president Lee DuBridge, who advised him to appeal the decision. Kármán, then in Europe, wrote to his student and offered to help, at the same time realizing that in a "time of unreason one could do little once these situations started, even with the strongest of auspices." To no avail, Kármán and his colleagues did try. DuBridge made appeals to associates in Washington and William Zisch, the president of Aerojet General, brought Tsien's case before the chief of Naval Intelligence. The Chinese scientist also visited Kármán's friend, Daniel Kimball, an Aerojet executive then serving as Undersecretary of the Navy. However, in the course of conversation, Tsien vowed to return to China if his clearance was not reinstated. Kimball panicked and informed the U.S. Immigration Service of the meeting.

Despite the lack of "the slightest evidence against Tsien," when he attempted to make good on the threat he was taken into custody, searched, detained for fourteen days, and released only after posting an extravagant bail. Immigration officers seized all of his luggage but, in 1,800 pounds of books and notes, detected no classified material. Nonetheless, the scientist found himself prohibited from leaving America for five years, during which time the government hoped his knowledge of sensitive data would become obsolete. A proud man, he experienced intense periods of depression. Not surprisingly, in 1955, at the end of the waiting period, he returned to his homeland with his wife and children. There he became a leading figure in rocketry and eventually directed the Institute of Mechanics in Peking.

He and Kármán had little contact after 1955. Tsien may have believed that his mentor, well connected in Washington circles, had not done enough to defend him against the charges. Perhaps Tsien did not know that Kármán himself had been subjected to investigation. In 1951, the FBI questioned the Hungarian on his service as a minister in the Communist Béla Kun regime. More grotesque, late in 1954, when his security clearance required renewal the Atomic Energy Commission balked at updating it, despite his frequent AGARD travels. Even though Lt. Gen. Donald Putt supported its reissuance, Kármán still was obliged to submit written statements attesting to his loyalty and anti-Communism. Like China, Hungary had adopted a Communist government, raising groundless suspicions in the minds of AEC and FBI officers aware of the many sensitive projects Kármán had undertaken. These interrogations not only tested his allegience to America, but also to Tsien, Frank Malina, Martin Summerfield, and even his sister.

The Boss testified he was not as familiar with Summerfield as with the other two men—whom he called his "students and close collaborators"—but had "no reason at the time to doubt [Summerfield's] loyalty." The GALCIT director said he learned of the charges against Malina from the newspapers and of those against Tsien only after his arrest by Immigration officials. Clearly, Kármán implied that since he had no reason to question Summerfield, he must surely trust Tsien and Malina, his most intimate pupils. In the same affadavit, he also denounced "as an inexcusable insult against me and the memory of my beloved sister" imputations of Pipö's Communist sympathies. He offered to relinquish his clearance if denied free movement among the NATO nations. Luckily, his access to classified materials was continued. But in his quiet way, Kármán showed courage in rebuffing false accusations and did, at some risk to himself, "do what [he] could" to protect the honor of Tsien, his other students, and his sister.

Kármán, *Wind and Beyond,* 308–14; Maj. Gen. Joseph F. Carroll to Lt. Gen. Donald L. Putt, November 26, 1954, USAFA; Putt to Carroll, n.d., USAFA; Kármán to Putt, December 22, 1954, USAFA, and enclosure: "Statements of Theodore von Kármán Requested in the Letter of the U.S.A.E.C., dated October 13, 1954," December 20, 1954.

10. Malina, "Rocket Research and Development," 6–9; Malina, "Memoir on GALCIT Rocket Research," 5, 11; interview, Malina with Hall; Koppes, *JPL and the American Space Program,* 5; interview, Lewis with Wilson, June 15, 1972.

11. Kármán, *Wind and Beyond,* 239; Millikan, "Kármán—His American Period," 616; Malina, "Rocket Research and Development," 9–11; Malina, "Memoir on Rocket Research," 11–12.

12. Malina, "Rocket Research and Development," 12; Malina, "Memoir on Rocket Research," 13–14; Kármán, *Wind and Beyond,* 240.

13. Kármán, *Wind and Beyond,* 242; Malina, "Memoir on Rocket Research," 15–17; Malina, "Rocket Research and Development," 12–19; "Plan to Plumb Space with Rocket Told," *Los Angeles Times,* January 26, 1938; Frank J. Malina, "Rocketry in California: Plans and Progress of the GALCIT Rocket Research Group," *Astronautics* (July 1938): 3–6.

14. Interview, Kármán with Shaughnessy; interview, Pickering with Gorn, December 27, 1989; interview, Sears with Gorn, February 6, 1990; Michael H. Gorn, "A Marriage of Convenience: Theodore von Kármán and U.S. Airpower, 1938–1958," presented on March 24, 1990, at a joint meeting of the Organization of American Historians and Society for History in the Federal Government in Washington, D.C.; Kármán, *Wind and Beyond,* 243; Kármán, "JATO," 377; Sears, "Some Recollections," 7 (see chap. 1, n. 1).

15. Interview, Kármán with Shaughnessy; Kármán, *Wind and Beyond,* 243; Gorn, "A Marriage of Convenience."

16. Kármán, *Wind and Beyond,* 242–43; Malina, "Rocket Research and Development," 19, 21–22; Frank J. Malina, "A Short Chronology of Rocket Research at the Jet Propulsion Laboratory 1936–1946," January 30, 1963, p. 1, JPL; Theodore von Kármán, "Assisted Take-off of Aircraft," a review of Rear Admiral Calvin M. Bolster's published lecture on JATOs (Norwich University, Northfield, Vermont, Publication No. 9, 1950) *American Rocket Society Journal* (June 1956): 92–93; Malina, "Memoir of Rocket Research," 17.

17. Kármán, *Wind and Beyond,* 241–43; Malina, "Rocket Research and Development," 22; Malina, "Memoir of Rocket Research," 17–18.

18. Kármán, "JATO," 377; Kármán, *Wind and Beyond,* 243; *GALCIT: The First Ten Years,* 18–19 (see chap. 3, n. 30); Malina, "Short Chronology," 1; Hall, "Shaping Aeronautics," 376 (see chap. 1, n. 2); interview, Kármán with

Shaughnessy; Frank J. Malina, "Memorial: Theodore von Kármán, 1881–1963," *Technology and Culture* (1964): 243 (hereafter Malina, "Kármán"); Wattendorf and Malina, "Kármán," 85 (see chap. 1, n. 3); Goldstein, "Kármán," 343; Malina, "Rocket Research and Development," 23–24; Malina, "Memoir of Rocket Research," 18–19; Frank J. Malina, "Report on Jet Propulsion for the National Academy of Science Committee on Air Corps Research," December 21, 1938, JPL; interview, Kármán with unknown interviewer, January 13, 1958, JPL.

19. Frank J. Malina, "The U.S. Army Air Corps Jet Propulsion Research Project, GALCIT Project No. 1, 1939–1946: A Memoir" (presented at the Third History Symposium of the IAA), 157 (in R. Cargill Hall, ed., *History of Rocketry and Astronautics; Proceedings of the Third through the Sixth Symposium of the International Academy of Astronautics,* AAS History Series 7, Pt. 2 [International Academy of Astronautics History Symposia, Vol. 2] [San Diego: Univelt, Inc., 1986]); Malina, "Rocket Research and Development," 26–27; Kármán, *Wind and Beyond,* 240; Edson, "He Tamed the Wind," 78 (see chap. 1, n. 7); Millikan, "Kármán—His American Period," 616; Halacy, *Supersonic Flight,* 107–11.

20. Malina, "Rocket Research and Development," 27; Malina, "GALCIT Project No. 1," 158; Theodore von Kármán, "Proposal for a Jet Propulsion Experimental Station at GALCIT," April 18, 1939, JPL; Theodore von Kármán, "Supplementary Proposal for a Jet Propulsion Experimental Station at GALCIT," May 31, 1939, JPL.

21. Malina, "Rocket Research and Development," 28; Malina, "GALCIT Project No. 1," 158; Kármán, *Wind and Beyond,* 244.

22. The findings of Kármán and Malina on solid rocket fuel first appeared in print in "Characteristics of the Ideal Solid Propellant Rocket Motor, Air Corps Jet Propulsion Research, GALCIT Project No. 1, Report No. 4," December 1, 1940; Goldstein, "Kármán," 342; Malina, "Rocket Research and Development," 31, 34; Hall, "Shaping Aeronautics," 377; Kármán, *Wind and Beyond,* 244–46; Wattendorf and Malina, "Kármán," 85; interview, Lewis with Wilson; interview, Malina with Hall; Malina, "GALCIT Project No. 1," 163–64; Malina, "Short Chronology," 2.

23. Frank J. Malina, John W. Parsons, and Edward S. Forman, "Final Report for 1939–1940, Air Corps Jet Propulsion Research, GALCIT Project No. 1, Report No. 3," June 15, 1940, JPL; Kármán, "Assisted Take-off," 93; Malina, "Rocket Research and Development," 33; Theodore von Kármán, "Program for Jet Propulsion Research at the California Institute of Technology, 1940–1941" (submitted to the National Academy of Sciences Subcommittee for Jet Propulsion Research, April 18, 1939, revised June 1, 1940), JPL.

24. Kármán, "Program for Jet Propulsion Research"; Malina, "Rocket Research and Development," 33–36; Malina, "GALCIT Project No. 1," 158; Theodore von Kármán, "Description of the Experimental Station of the Air

Corps Jet Propulsion Research Project, GALCIT Project No. 1, Report No. 6," February 26, 1941, JPL.

25. Malina, "Rocket Research and Development," 38; Kármán, *Wind and Beyond,* 249–51; Malina, "GALCIT Project No. 1," 183–87.

26. Malina, "Rocket Research and Development," 37, 39–42; Theodore von Kármán, "Proposed 1942–1943 Program for the Air Corps Jet Propulsion Research Project, GALCIT Project No. 1," May 30, 1942, JPL; Malina, "GALCIT Project No. 1," 194; Kármán, *Wind and Beyond,* 256–58; interview, Malina with Hall; Aerojet Engineering, "The Promise and the Performance," 1948, 1, JPL; interview, Kármán with Thomas, January 12, 1960.

27. Kármán, *Wind and Beyond,* 258–60; Malina, "Rocket Research and Development," 42–47; interview, Malina with Hall; Malina, "GALCIT Project No. 1," 194–95; Kármán, "Assisted Take-off," 93; Koppes, *JPL and the American Space Program,* 16.

28. Malina, "Rocket Research and Development," 47; Gorn, "A Marriage of Convenience"; Sears, "Some Recollections," 5–7; interview, Thomas Vrebalovich with M. Gorn, Los Angeles, February 13, 1990 (by telephone).

**CHAPTER 6. A WARTIME MISSION**

1. Interview, Sears with Gorn, February 6, 1990; Halacy, *Supersonic Flight,* 117 (see chap. 1, n. 7); Kármán, *Wind and Beyond,* 176 (see chap. 1, n. 1); Goldstein, "Kármán," 343 (see chap. 1, n. 2).

2. Malina, "Rocket Research and Development," 48, 50–52 (see chap. 5, n. 5); Kármán, *Wind and Beyond,* 315–17; Millikan, "Kármán—His American Period," 616 (see chap. 1, n. 1); Andrew Haley, "Aerojet Engineering Corporation, Its Background, Objectives, and Accomplishments," ca. May 21, 1944, 6–10, JPL.

3. Theodore von Kármán and Frank J. Malina, "Air Corps Jet Propulsion Research, GALCIT Project No. 1, Progress Report 4, Facilities and Equipment of the Air Corps Jet Propulsion Research Project," May 28, 1943, 1–2, 7, 24, 43, 44, JPL; Frank J. Malina, "America's First Long-Range Missile and Space Exploration Program: The ORDCIT Project of the Jet Propulsion Laboratory, 1943–46: A Memoir," in *History of Rocketry and Astronautics,* ed. R. Cargill Hall, 343–44 (see chap. 5, n. 19, for a full citation of this work); Theodore von Kármán, "The Possibilities of Long Range Rocket Projectiles, Memorandum JPL-1," November 20, 1943, 1–3, JPL; Col. G. W. Trichel to Kármán, January 15, 1944, JPL; Frank J. Malina (for Theodore von Kármán) to JPL section chiefs, August 18, 1944, JPL; Theodore von Kármán, "ORDCIT Memorandum No. 2, Research Program for the Second Type of Long Range Jet Propelled Missile," August 20, 1944, JPL; "JPL, GALCIT Directory," 1945, JPL; interview, Kármán with unknown interviewer, January 13, 1958; Malina, "Short Chronology," 3 (see chap. 5, n. 16).

4. Kármán, *Wind and Beyond,* 262; Malina, "Rocket Research and Development," 33, 56, 58; Halacy, *Supersonic Flight,* 132–33; interview, Kármán with Shaughnessy, January 27, 1960.

5. Interview, Kármán with Shaughnessy; Kármán, *Wind and Beyond,* 267–68; Michael H. Gorn, *Harnessing the Genie: Science and Technology Forecasting for Air Force, 1944–1986* (Washington, D.C.: Office of Air Force History, 1988), 12; *New York Times,* September 8, 9, 10, and 11, 1944, 1. Thomas Sturm, *The USAF Scientific Advisory Board: Its First Twenty Years, 1944–1964* (Washington, D.C.: USAF Historical Division Liaison Office, 1967; rpt., Washington, D.C.: Office of Air Force History, 1986), 2–3; Henry H. Arnold, *Global Mission* (New York: Harper and Row, 1949; rpt., Blue Ridge Summit, Pa.: TAB Books, 1989), 532; Halacy, *Supersonic Flight,* 133.

6. Interview, Kármán with Shaughnessy; Malina, "Rocket Research and Development," 58; Kármán, *Wind and Beyond,* 268.

7. Nick A. Komons, *Science and the Air Force: A History of the Air Force Office of Scientific Research* (Arlington, Va.: Historical Division, Office of Information, Office of Aerospace Research, 1966), 2–3. Kármán, *Wind and Beyond,* 268; interview, Kármán with Shaughnessy; interview, Dr. Hugh L. Dryden with Donald Shaughnessy, February 23, 1960, AFHRC; interview, Gen. James K. Doolittle with unknown interviewer, April 21, 1969, Office of Air Force History files, p. 9 (hereafter abbreviated as OAFH); Courtland D. Perkins, "U.S. Air Force Scientific Advisory Board," in "Recollections" (unpublished manuscript), chap. 7, pp. 1–2, U.S. Air Force Scientific Advisory Board files (hereafter abbreviated as SAB); interview, Gen. Bernard A. Schriever with Jacob Neufeld, Washington, D.C., December 19, 1989, OAFH; interview, Sears with Gorn, February 6, 1990; Sears, "Kármán," 7; interview, Vrebalovich with Gorn, February 13, 1990.

8. Malina, "Rocket Research and Development," 61; Kármán, *Wind and Beyond,* 268; Millikan, "Kármán—His American Period," 617; Dryden, "Theodore von Kármán," 356 (see chap. 1, n. 18); Sturm, *USAF Scientific Advisory Board,* 4; Col. F. M. Dean to Kármán, October 9, 1944, TVK 90.1.

9. Kármán to Clark Millikan, November 4, 1944, TVK 73.6; Vladimir K. Zworykin to Kármán, November 2, 1944, TVK 33.26; Theodore F. Walkowicz, "Von Kármán's Singular Contributions to U.S. Aerospace Power," *Air Force Magazine,* May 1981, 60; interview, Kármán with Shaughnessy; Kármán, *Wind and Beyond,* 268–69. Lt. Gen. Barney M. Giles to generals Timberlake, Owens, Smith, Norstad, et. al., November 10, 1944, SAB.

10. Walkowicz, "Kármán's Contributions," 60–61; Henry H. Arnold to Kármán, November 7, 1944, SAB.

11. Giles to Timberlake et al.

12. The Scientific Advisory Group consultants included Drs. Charles W. Bray (Princeton), Lee A. DuBridge (Cal Tech), Pol Duwez (Cal Tech),

George A. Gamow (Johns Hopkins), Ivan A. Getting (MIT), Lewis P. Hammett (Explosives Research Laboratory), Walter S. Hunter (Brown), Irving P. Krick (Cal Tech), Duncan P. MacDougall (Naval Ordnance Lab), George A. Morton (Naval Research Center), Nathan M. Newmark (Illinois), William H. Pickering (Cal Tech), Edward M. Purcell (Harvard), Galen B. Schubauer (National Bureau of Standards), William R. Sears (Cornell), Arthur J. Stosick (Cal Tech), William J. Sweeney (Standard Oil), George F. Valley, Jr. (MIT), Fritz Zwicky (Cal Tech), Vladimir K. Zworykin (RCA Labs), Irving L. Ashkenas (Northrop Aircraft), and W. Randolph Lovelace, II (the Lovelace Foundation). Kármán to Arnold, November 20, 1944, TVK 90.1; H. S. Tsien, "Outline of a Report on Trends of Development of Military Aircraft," November 26, 1944, TVK 30.37; "AAF Long Range Development Program, Management Control, Commitments, and Requirements," November 22, 1944, OAFH; Headquarters Office Instruction No. 20-76, "Organization: The AAF Scientific Advisory Group," December 1944, SAB; Gorn, *Genie,* 18–20; Sturm, *USAF Scientific Advisory Board,* 5.

13. Arnold, *Global Mission,* 533; H. S. Tsien, C. C. Lin, W. Z. Chien, and Y. H. Kuo to Kármán, November 7, 1944, TVK 30.37; Malina, "Rocket Research and Development," 61; Kármán to Arnold, November 20, 1944, TVK 90.1; Kármán, *Wind and Beyond,* 271.

14. Sturm, *USAF Scientific Advisory Board,* 5. Kármán to Arnold, April 30, 1945, TVK 90.2; "AAF Scientific Advisory Group Organization Chart," March 1, 1945, OAFH; Gorn, *Genie,* 18, 21–22.

15. Arnold to Kármán, November 7, 1944, SAB; Dr. Frank L. Wattendorf to Col. Frederic Glantzberg, December 6, 1944, TVK 90.1; Brig. Gen. Frederic H. Smith, Jr., to the AAF Assistant Chief of Staff, Operations, December 16, 1944, TVK 90.1; Lt. I. W. Mitchnick to Lt. Col. Carr, December 14, 1944, TVK 90.1; Maj. Gen. J. E. Hull to Gen. H. Arnold, December 24, 1944, TVK 90.1.

16. Giles to Gen. George C. Marshall, February 13, 1945, TVK 90.2.

17. Clearance for foreign visits of the Scientific Advisory Group and itinerary, February 17, 1945, TVK 90.2; Maj. O. W. Hammonds to Glantzberg, February 19, 1945, TVK 90.2; Giles to AC/AS, Intelligence Collection Division, April 3, 1945, TVK 90.2; Giles to whom it may concern, April 11, 1945, TVK 90.2; Glantzberg to Commissioner of Immigration and Naturalization, April 17, 1945; Arnold to Spaatz, April 19, 1945, TVK 90.2; Headquarters Air Force Systems Command History Office files (hereafter abbreviated as AFSC/HO.

18. Minutes of Scientific Advisory Group meeting, August 29, 1945, 3–4, OAFH; Brig. Gen. George C. McDonald to unknown correspondent, April 22, 1945, AFHRC; Kármán, *Wind and Beyond,* 272–75; Weekly Activity Report, Director of Intelligence, HQ USSTAF, May 4, 1945, AFHRC; Weekly

Activity Report, Exploitation Division, HQ USSTAF, May 19, 1945, ARHRC; Sturm, *USAF Scientific Advisory Board,* 6; Hammonds to Arnold, April 24, 1945, AFSC/HO; "Itinerary of Von Kármán's Mission to Europe," n.d., AFSC/HO; Richard Rhodes, *The Making of the Atomic Bomb* (New York: Simon and Schuster, 1986), 605–10.

19. Kármán, *Wind and Beyond,* 277–83; Daily Activity Reports, Exploitation Division, HQ USSTAF, May 30 and 31, 1945, AFHRC; Sturm, *USAF Scientific Advisory Board,* 6; Weekly Activity Report, Exploitation Division, HQ USSTAF, May 31, 1945, AFHRC; Kármán to Colonel H. M. McCoy, July 13, 1945, AFSC/HO; Kármán to Arnold, July 30, 1945, AFSC/HO; Walkowicz, "Kármán's Contributions," 61; interview, Dr. H. Guyford Stever with M. Gorn, Washington, D.C., April 1987, Air Force Oral History Program, AFHRC.

20. Daily Activity Reports, Exploitation Division, HQ USSTAF, June 18 and 19, 1945, AFHRC; Weekly Activity Report, HQ USSTAF, June 22, 1945, AFHRC; Daily Activity Report, USSTAF Main Supply Section, June 25, 1945, AFHRC; Lt. Gen. Ira C. Eaker to Kármán, July 18, 1945, TVK 90.2; George W. Lewis to Arnold, June 30, 1945, TVK 90.2

21. "Itinerary of Von Kármán's Mission to Europe"; Weekly Activity Report, Exploitation Division, HQ USSTAF, June 14, 1945, AFHRC; Kármán, *Wind and Beyond,* 283–89; minutes of a Scientific Advisory Group meeting, August 29, 1945, 9, OAFH.

22. Daily Activity Report, Exploitation Division, HQ USSTAF, June 13, 1945, AFHRC; Kármán, *Wind and Beyond,* 289; Sturm, *USAF Scientific Advisory Board,* 7–8; Theodore von Kármán, *Where We Stand* (AAF Scientific Advisory Group, August 1944), iv, AFSC/HO; Walkowicz, "Kármán's Contributions," 62.

23. Kármán, *Where We Stand,* 1–7.

24. Ibid., 9–17.

25. Ibid., 18–35.

26. Ibid., 36–37.

27. Ibid., 41, 48–54

**CHAPTER 7. ADVISING THE GENERALS**

1. Sturm, *USAF Scientific Advisory Board,* 8 (see chap. 6, n. 5); Kármán, *Wind and Beyond,* 289–90 (see chap. 1, n. 1).

2. Lt. Col. Godfrey McHugh to members of the Scientific Advisory Group going overseas, August 29, 1945; McHugh to the commanding general, Army Services Forces, August 31, 1945; Request for Orders for Civilian Personnel, August 31, 1945; Dr. Fritz Zwicky to Kármán, September 4, 1945; Kármán to Zwicky, September 20, 1945; memo for the Commanding General, Air Transport Command, September 17, 1945; Eaker to Lt. Gen. George C.

Kenney, September 6, 1945; Arnold to whom it may concern, September 21, 1945: all TVK 90.3. Walkowicz, "Kármán's Contributions," 62 (see chap. 6, n. 9).

3. Kármán, *Wind and Beyond,* 290–91. Kármán to an unknown correspondent, October 10, 1945; Request for Orders for Mr. Henry Nagamatsu, Dr. Fritz Zwicky, and Col. W. Randolph Lovelace, October 16, 1945; unknown correspondent to Colonel Glantzberg, October 23, 1945; Kármán to Arnold, October 29, 1945: all TVK 90.3. Walkowicz, "Kármán's Contributions," 62; interview, Stever with Gorn, April 1987.

4. Kármán to Hugh L. Dryden, November 7, 9, and 22, 1945, TVK 90.3; Walkowicz, "Kármán's Contributions," 62.

5. Kármán, *Wind and Beyond,* 291–94; Theodore von Kármán, *Science, the Key to Air Supremacy,* Vol. 1 of *Toward New Horizons* (AAF Scientific Advisory Group, December 15, 1944), xxi–xxiii, AFSC/HO; minutes of a Scientific Advisory Group meeting, December 5, 1945, p. 1, OAFH.

6. Kármán to Arnold, December 15, 1945, SAB.

7. Kármán, *Science,* 1–4.

8. Ibid., 81–82, 85, 87, 91, 95, 97, 101, 104, 107, 108–9.

9. Tsien, "Outline of a Report on Trends," November 26, 1944 (see chap. 6, n. 12); Kármán to Arnold, April 30, 1945, TVK 90.2; Wattendorf to Gen. Frank O. Carroll, June 19, 1945, TVK 87.1.

10. Interview, Kármán with Shaughnessy, January 27, 1960; Maj. Gen. Curtis LeMay to unknown correspondent, June 14, 1946, OAFH; Lt. Gen. Nathan F. Twining to Arnold, May 8, 1946, OAFH; "Recommendations of Vol. I by the Army Air Forces Scientific Advisory Group," April 9, 1946, OAFH files; Kármán, *Wind and Beyond,* 291, 294; Sturm, *USAF Scientific Advisory Board,* 10–11. Brig. Gen. Laurence C. Craigie to Gen. Carl Spaatz, March 1, 1946; Col. Donald L. Putt to Spaatz, March 13, 1946; Kármán to the Commanding General, Air Technical Services Command, March 15, 1946: all TVK 90.4. Maj. Ted Walkowicz to Mrs. Marie Roddenberry, July 11, 1946, TVK 31.38.

11. Robert Frank Futrell, *Ideas, Concepts, and Doctrine: A History of Basic Thinking in the USAF, 1907–1964* (Maxwell AFB, Ala.: Air University Publications, 1971), 111–12; Sturm, *USAF Scientific Advisory Board,* 11–12; interview, Dr. Ivan Getting with M. Gorn, Washington, D.C., March 12, 1986; Kármán, *Wind and Beyond,* 291–94.

12. Kármán, *Wind and Beyond,* 294; Kármán to Arnold, December 20, 1944, SAB.

13. Kármán to Arnold, January 9, 1946, SAB; Arnold to Spaatz, December 21, 1945, SAB; Lt. Gen. John K. Cannon to Arnold, December 27, 1945, TVK 90.3; Arnold to Maj. Gen. Edward H. Powers, January 3, 1946, SAB; LeMay to Spaatz, January 3, 1946, SAB; Sturm, *USAF Scientific Advisory Board,* 13–14.

14. Sturm, *USAF Scientific Advisory Board,* 13–15. LeMay to the Deputy Commander, Army Air Forces, February 13, 1946; Headquarters Office Instruction 20-76, "Organization—Army Air Forces Scientific Advisory Group," March 4, 1946; Dr. Edward L. Bowles to Eaker, March 5, 1946; Spaatz to Scientific Advisory Group members, March 14, 1946; Plan for SAB Operation, April 18, 1946: all SAB.

15. Gen. Dwight D. Eisenhower to directors and chiefs of the War Department general and special staff divisions, April 30, 1946, AFHRC.

16. Malina, "Rocket Research and Development," 69 (see chap. 5, n. 5); minutes of an SAB meeting, June 16, 1946, 1–5, OAFH; Sturm, *USAF Scientific Advisory Board,* 15–16, 137, 140; Kármán, *Wind and Beyond,* 298–99; LeMay to Kármán, March 12, 1946, TVK 87.1; Kármán to Spaatz, July 9, 1946, TVK 87.1; Headquarters Office Instruction 20-76, "Organization—the USAF Scientific Advisory Board," October 10, 1947, SAB; Kármán to Major Alexander, September 15, 1947, OAFH.

17. Interview, Getting with Gorn, March 12, 1986; Walkowicz to Kármán, October 14, 1947, TVK 31.38.

18. Craigie to Kármán, January 15, 1948, OAFH; minutes of an SAB meeting, March 17–18, 1948, p. 1, OAFH; Walkowicz to Kármán, October 14, 1947, TVK 31.38; Kármán to Spaatz, April 6, 1948, SAB; Marie A. Roddenberry to Memo for Record, April 15, 1948, SAB; Maj. Gen. William F. McKee to Air Staff Deputy Chief of Staff for Material, April 26, 1948, SAB; Air Force Regulation 20-30, "Organization—Scientific Advisory Board to the Chief of Staff, USAF," May 14, 1948, SAB.

19. Interview, Lt. Gen. Donald L. Putt with Dr. James C. Hasdorff, April 1–3, 1974, Air Force Oral History Program, AFHRC; Maj. J. C. DeHart to Putt, September 29, 1948, SAB; Kármán, *Wind and Beyond,* 303–4; Sturm, *USAF Scientific Advisory Board,* 31; Headquarters Air Research and Development Command Annual History, January 23, 1950 to June 30, 1951, 28–49 (AFSC/HO).

20. Sturm, *USAF Scientific Advisory Board,* 32–34; interview, Putt with Hasdorff, April 1–3, 1974; Headquarters Air Research and Development Command Annual History, January 23, 1950, to June 30, 1951, 28–49 (AFSC/HO); Kármán to Gen. Hoyt S. Vandenberg, January 15, 1949, OAFH; minutes of a Scientific Advisory Board meeting, April 7, 1949, p. 2, OAFH; Louis N. Ridenour, "Research and Development in the United States Air Force: Report of a Special Committee of the Scientific Advisory Board to the Chief of Staff, USAF," with an attached letter, Kármán to Vandenberg, September 21, 1949, AFSC/HO; Gen. Muir S. Fairchild to Headquarters Deputy Chiefs of Staff and Assistant Vice-Chiefs of Staff, January 23, 1950, OAFH.

21. "Biographical Sketch of Dr. Theodore von Kármán," n.d., AFSC/HO; "Britain Pays Honor to Scientist," Pasadena *Star News,* May 13, 1946; War Department press release, "Three Civilian Scientists Receive Awards from

AAF," June 10, 1946, USAFA; "Medal Recognizes Nation's Debt to Caltech Expert," Pasadena *Star News,* July 3, 1946; "Dr. von Kármán Named for '47 Fritz Medal," Pasadena *Star News,* January 23, 1947; Marie D. Roddenberry to Mrs. A. C. Slade, December 5, 1950, USAFA; Air Force Association news release, "Dr. von Kármán Receives Annual Science Award of the Air Force Association," December 15, 1950, USAFA; "This Month at Caltech: von Kármán's Travels," *Engineering and Science* [Cal Tech], April 1949, 14–15;

22. "Biographical Sketch"; "This Month at Caltech," 14–15; Wattendorf to Putt, May 11, 1950, USAFA; Maj. Gen. Gordon F. Saville to the Air Staff Deputy Chief of Staff, Personnel, June 27, 1950, USAFA; Saville to Vandenberg, April 18, 1951, USAFA.

23. Joseph V. Charyk to Sydney Goldstein, August 9, 1948, TVK 5.24; Clark B. Millikan, "Theodore von Kármán," *Journal of the Aeronautical Sciences* (May 1956): 404; Kármán, *Wind and Beyond,* 324–25; Perkins, "Recollections," chap. 9, p. 1 (see chap. 6, n. 7); Sturm, *USAF Scientific Advisory Board,* 49; Malina, "Kármán," 245 (see chap. 5, n. 18).

24. Kármán, *Wind and Beyond,* 329–30; Perkins, "Recollections," chap. 9, p. 1; Sturm, *USAF Scientific Advisory Board,* 49; Millikan, "Kármán," 404; Dryden, "Theodore von Kármán," 357 (see chap. 1, n. 18); Walkowicz, "Kármán's Contributions," 66.

25. Walkowicz, "Kármán's Contributions," 66; Kármán, *Wind and Beyond,* 326.

26. Vandenberg to Kármán, March 5, 1952, USAFA; Malina, "Kármán," 245; Kármán to Craigie, February 22, 1952, USAFA; Taylor, "Memories of Kármán," 480 (see chap. 1, n. 15); Kármán, *Wind and Beyond,* 329; Perkins, "Recollections," chap. 1, p. 2.

27. Perkins, "Recollections," chap. 1, p. 2; Wattendorf to B. S. Driscoll, May 2, 1952, USAFA; Kármán, *Wind and Beyond,* 329; Dryden, "Contributions," 15 (see chap. 1, n. 15); Millikan, "Kármán," 405; Dryden, "Theodore von Kármán," 357–58.

28. Wattendorf and Malina, "Kármán," 91 (see chap. 1, n. 3); Thomas, *Men of Space,* 1:177 (see chap. 1, n. 7); interview, Sears with Gorn, February 6, 1990; Kármán, *Wind and Beyond,* 331; Millikan, "Kármán," 405; Dryden, "Theodore von Kármán," 358; Perkins, "Recollections," chap. 1, p. 2.

## CHAPTER 8. THE ELDER STATESMAN

1. Kármán, *Wind and Beyond,* 327 (see chap. 1, n. 1); interview, Sears with Gorn, February 6, 1990; William Sears to Kármán, February 11, 1948, TVK 27.45; Malina, "Kármán," 246 (see chap. 5, n. 18); Walkowicz, "Kármán's Contributions," 67 (see chap. 6, n. 9); Thomas, *Men of Space,* 1:178 (see chap. 1, n. 7); Hugh L. Dryden, "The Contributions of Theodore von

Kármán to Science and Technology" in *Collected Works of Theodore von Kármán* (see chap. 2, n. 7), 1:ix.

2. Kármán, *Wind and Beyond,* iii, 100–101, 277, 327; Goldstein, "Kármán," 345 (see chap. 1, n. 2); Halacy, *Supersonic Flight,* 161 (see chap. 1, n. 7); Robert Cahn, "Dr. Theodore von Kármán, Gemütlicher Genius of Aeronautics," *Air Force Magazine* (October 1957): 48; Edson, "He Tamed the Wind," 78 (see chap. 1, n. 7); interview, Sears with Gorn.

3. Chester N. Hasert to Kármán, May 13, 1954, USAFA; Maj. Daniel Whitcraft to Kármán, June 21, 1954, USAFA; James H. Doolittle to Kármán, January 15, 1953, USAFA; Lt. Gen. Thomas D. White to Kármán, June 8, 1953, USAFA; Hasert to Kármán, May 21, 1954, USAFA; Hasert to Kármán, August 19, 1953, USAFA; Hasert to Kármán, September 20, 1954, USAFA; Theodore von Kármán's passport, issued June 23, 1953, USAFA; "Dr. Von Kármán Back from Paris Duty," Pasadena *Star News,* February 17, 1954; Sturm, *USAF Scientific Advisory Board,* 50 (see chap. 6, n. 5); Kármán to Gen. Nathan F. Twining, September 17, 1954, USAFA; Whitcraft to Thomas A. Lamphier, November 3, 1954, USAFA; "Dr. von Kármán Gets Wright Brothers Trophy," Pasadena *Star News,* December 6, 1954; Putt to Kármán, February 23, December 6 and 30, 1954, TVK 24.10; Twining to Kármán, December 31, 1954, USAFA.

4. Doolittle to Kármán, February 1 and 23, 1956, USAFA; Kármán to Putt, October 10, 1955, TVK 24.10; Brig. Gen. Bernard A. Schriever to Lt. Gen. Thomas S. Power, April 11, 1955, USAFA; "Request for Personnel Action" (Air Force Form 52): forms filed by Kármán for consulting services, June 1, 1955, to May 7, 1963, USAFA; "Scientist Receives Presidential Medal," Pasadena *Star News,* June 21, 1956; General Order 31, Department of the Air Force, "Medal of Freedom Award," May 31, 1956, USAFA.

5. Putt to Craigie, November 24, 1953, OAFH; "Presentation by Lt. Gen. D. L. Putt . . . for the USAF Scientific Advisory Board . . . on October 19, 1953," 15–16, OAFH.

6. Kármán, *Wind and Beyond,* 305; Hasert to Whitcraft, December 3, 1953, OAFH; Kármán to SAB panel chairmen, January 29, 1954, OAFH.

7. "Long Range R&D Planning and Inter-action of Technology and Strategy," January 18, 1954, OAFH; "Proposed Draft of Address by the Chief of Staff, USAF, to the Scientific Advisory Board, Langley Air Force Base, March 22, 1954," OAFH; seven reports, all dated March 23, 1954: "Preliminary Report on the Explosives and Armament Panel of New Horizons," "Preliminary Report of the Geophysical Panel on New Horizons," "Preliminary Report of the Fuels and Propulsion Panel on New Horizons," "Preliminary Report of the Intelligence Systems Panel on New Horizons," "Preliminary Report of the Social Sciences Panel on New Horizons," "Preliminary Report of the Nuclear Weapons Panel on New Horizons," "Preliminary Report of the Electronics and

Communications Panel on New Horizons," OAFH; Hasert to Kármán, May 13, 1954, USAFA; Sturm, *USAF Scientific Advisory Board,* 56–62, 64; Whitcraft to Kármán, June 21, 1954, USAFA; Doolittle to Putt, September 29, 1954, OAFH; "Some Remarks of the Electronics and Communications Panel on New Technical Developments in the Next Ten Years," October 1, 1954, OAFH; "Some Remarks on the Aircraft Panel on New Technical Developments of the Next Ten Years," October 1, 1954, OAFH; "Some Remarks of the Aeromedical Panel on New Developments of the Next Ten Years," October 1, 1954, OAFH.

8. Kenneth McAlpine to David C. Hazen, Courtland Perkins, and H. Guyford Stever, February 11, 1983, National Academy of Sciences Archives (hereafter abbreviated as NAS); "Woods Hole Conference Maps Long-Range AF Plans," *Astronautics* (September 1957): 4.

9. Walkowicz, "Kármán's Contributions," 67; National Academy of Sciences Governing Board Agenda, December 9, 1956, "Proposed Study of the Scientific and Technological Future of the Air Force," NAS; Kármán, *Wind and Beyond,* 305; McAlpine to Hazen et al., February 22, 1983; Lt. Col. Floyd J. Sweet to Kármán, April 26, 1957, TVK 90.11.

10. Kármán to advisory council (draft, n.d.), NAS; "Woods Hole Conference," 4; McAlpine to Hazen et al., February 22, 1983; Kármán, *Wind and Beyond,* 305; Detlev V. Bronk to potential New Horizon members, April 22, 1957, NAS; John S. Coleman to William R. Sears, December 9, 1957, NAS.

11. McAlpine to Hazen et al., February 22, 1983; Kármán to advisory council (draft, n.d.), NAS; Bronk to potential New Horizon members, April 22, 1957; "Woods Hole Conference," 4; "Summary Report of the NAS-ARDC Study Group Relating to Long-Range Scientific and Technical Trends of Interest to the United States Air Force," National Academy of Sciences, 1958, 66–69, AFSC/HO (hereafter referred to as the Woods Hole Summer Study); National Academy of Sciences Contract No. AF 18 (600)-1661 with Air Research and Development Command for a "Scientific Investigatory Group to Conduct Long-Range Studies," May 6, 1957, NAS; Kármán to Ivan Getting, June 4, 1957, NAS.

12. "Nation's Foremost Scientists to Forecast Future Air Force Research and Development Needs," Air Research and Development Command Office of Information Services, June 24, 1957, NAS; NAS Contract No. AF 18(600)-1661, May 6, 1957, NAS; "Remarks by H. Guyford Stever," June 24, 1957, NAS; "Remarks by Gen. D. L. Putt," June 24, 1957, NAS; "Remarks by the Honorable James H. Douglas," June 24, 1957, NAS; "Remarks by Major General Howell M. Estes, Jr.," June 25, 1957, NAS.

13. Kármán to advisory council (draft, n.d.); Kármán, *Wind and Beyond,* 306; Kármán to Getting, June 4, 1957, NAS; S. D. Cornell to Peregrine White, October 21, 1957, NAS; Detlev Bronk to Gen. Thomas D. White, May 6, 1957, NAS.

14. John S. Coleman to Dr. Allen E. Puckett, May 28, 1957, NAS; "Proprietary Rights," n.d., NAS; Kármán, *Wind and Beyond,* 306; Gen. Samuel E. Anderson to Stever, September 12, 1957, NAS.

15. Woods Hole Summer Study, 1958, 66–69, AFSC/HO; Supplemental Agreement to Contract No. AF 18(600)-1661 between the National Academy of Sciences and the Air Research and Development Command for additional time and work funds, March 3, 1958, NAS; Coleman to Sears, December 9, 1957, NAS; B. J. Driscoll to project participants (draft), March 3(?), 1958, NAS; Driscoll to Bronk, February 5, 1958, NAS; Walkowicz to Driscoll, February 5, 1958, NAS; Richard S. Cesaro to Wattendorf, January 23, 1958, NAS; Driscoll to Kármán, March 4, 1958, TVK 7.25; Driscoll to Bronk, May 14, 1958, NAS.

16. Driscoll to Bronk, February 5, 1958; Driscoll to William J. Harris, Jr., February 26, 1958; Driscoll to Coleman, April 15, 1958; Driscoll to Bronk, May 14, 1958; "NAS-ARDC Study Project Schedule for June 26th and 27th," June 25, 1958; Driscoll to Fred E. Fiedler, June 6, 1958; Cesaro to Wattendorf, December 23, 1957: all NAS.

17. Kármán to members of the 1958 study group, May 1958, NAS.

18. Kármán to John H. Holloman, May 21, 1958; Kármán to Sears, May 16, 1958; Sears to Kármán, June 3, 1958: all NAS.

19. Kármán to Sears, May 16, 1958; Driscoll to Walkowicz, January 21, 1958, NAS; Kármán to Woods Hole members, July 25 and August 20, 1958, NAS; Sears to Woods Hole members, August 26, 1958, NAS; Kármán to Woods Hole Committee chairmen, August 12, 1958, NAS.

20. Driscoll to Dr. Frederick C. Frick, October 27, 1958, NAS; "Program Outline for Committees 1-2," July 1, 1958, NAS; Driscoll to Mrs. Mary McGilvray, December 19, 1958, NAS; Gorn, *Genie,* 76–78 (see chap. 6, n. 5).

21. "Preliminary Agenda for USAF Briefing on Results of Study Project," November 18, 1958, NAS; Woods Hole Summer Study, 1958, 60–62, 51, 47–49, 53–55, 64–65, 4–10, 11–19, 20–27, 28–31, 45, AFSC/HO.

22. Anderson to Bronk, August 4, 1958, NAS: Bronk to Schriever, May 13, 1959, NAS; Schriever to Bronk, May 29, 1959, and February 29, 1960, NAS; Driscoll to Kármán, September 22, 1958, TVK 7.25; Kármán, *Wind and Beyond,* 307.

**CHAPTER 9.** "HIS LIFE WAS FULL"

1. Theodore von Kármán's passport, issued June 23, 1953, USAFA; Theodore von Kármán's Scientific Advisory Board identification card, n.d., USAFA; Lee Edson and A. K. Oppenheim, "Von Kármániana," *Astronautics* (June 1958): 43; Lee Edson and A. K. Oppenheim, "Von Kármániana—Part II," *Astronautics* (June 1958): 41, 44.

2. Theodore von Kármán, "Engineering Education in Our Age," presented by Theodore von Kármán to the Institute of the Aeronautical Sciences Northeastern Student Conference, April 4, 1959, at Cornell University (reprinted by the IAS); Theodore von Kármán, "From Newton's Notebook to Mammoth Research Organizations," *Interavia* (March 1952): 131–32; Theodore von Kármán, "A Few Comments on Rocketry," *Interavia* (November 1953): 628–29; Theodore von Kármán, "The Next Fifty Years," *Interavia* (January 1955): 19–20; Theodore von Kármán, "Faster, Higher, Hotter," *Interavia* (June 1956): 407; Theodore von Kármán, "Some Observations on Guided Missiles," *Interavia* (August 1957): 777–78; Theodore von Kármán, "More or Less Seriously," *Interavia* (December 1957): 1227–28; Kármán, *Aerodynamics,* 203 (see chap. 2, n. 10); Kármán, *Wind and Beyond,* 327–28 (see chap. 1, n. 1); Theodore von Kármán and Shih I. Pai, *From Low Speed Aerodynamics to Astronautics* (New York: Macmillan, 1963), 51.

3. U.S. Congress, Senate Congressional Record, May 3, 1961, 6587–88; U.S. Congress, House Congressional Record, May 11, 1961, 7361; "Von Kármán Busy at 80," Baltimore *Sun,* May 7, 1961; news release from the Institute of the Aerospace Sciences: Von Kármán press conference, May 8, 1961, AFSC/HO; Associated Press coverage of von Kármán press conference, May 9, 1961, AFSC/HO; United Press International coverage of von Kármán press conference, May 9, 1961, AFSC/HO; William Grigg, "Von Kármán at 80 Has Keen Vision on Space," Washington *Evening Star,* May 10, 1961; John Troan, "Missiles Fired From Trucks 'Ideal' Weapon, Scientist Says," Cincinnati *Post and Times-Star,* May 11, 1961; "Serious Space Gap Is Doubted: World Authority Believes It Is Not Great," Baltimore *Sun,* May 10, 1961; John G. Norris, "Air-Breathing Orbital Planes Urged By Expert As Cheaper than Rockets," Washington *Post and Time Herald,* May 10, 1961; "The Team of Genius and Courage," Knoxville *News-Sentinel,* May 10, 1961.

4. News release from the Institute of the Aerospace Sciences: von Kármán symposium and banquet, May 7, 1961, AFSC/HO; "Organizations Invited to Participate in . . . Anniversary of Theodore von Kármán," n.d., USAFA; *Proceedings of an Aerospace Scientific Symposium of Distinguished Lectures in Honor of Dr. Theodore von Kármán on His Eightieth Anniversary, May 11, 1961,* sponsored by the Air Force Office of Scientific Research (New York: Institute of the Aerospace Sciences), 1962, iv, v, 1, 87, 111–20.

5. "The Th. vK. Guest List," n.d., USAFA; Program of "The Theodore von Kármán Eightieth Anniversary Banquet," May 11, 1961, USAFA; *Proceedings* of AFOSR Symposium in honor of Kármán, 121–27; Irwin Hersey, "Von Kármán at 80," *Astronautics* (July 1961): 48, 89; "JFK, World Scientists Honor Air Pioneer von Kármán," Oakland *Tribune,* May 12, 1961; Helen Waterhouse, "Former Guggenheim Director Honored," Akron *Beacon Journal,* May 21, 1961.

6. "Von Kármán Predicts Atom Rockets," *NATO Journal* (September 1961): 23; "Award of the James Watt International Medal to Professor Dr. Theodore von Kármán," September 13, 1961, USAFA; Kármán, *Wind and Beyond,* 3, 11, 12; "Science Honor Paid Pasadena: Kennedy Lauds Von Kármán," Pasadena *Star News,* January 1, 1963; "National Medal of Science," *Physics Today* (April 1963): 102; Robert C. Toth, "Von Kármán Gets U.S. Science Prize: Kennedy Gives First Such Medal to Aerodynamicist," *New York Times,* February 19, 1963.

7. "Science Honor Paid Pasadena," Pasadena *Star News;* Kármán, *Wind and Beyond,* 3, 12; Toth, "Kármán Gets Prize"; Robert Thompson "A 'First' for Science: Kennedy Hails Dr. von Kármán," Los Angeles *Times,* February 19, 1963.

8. Toth, "Kármán Gets Prize"; Thompson, "A 'First' for Science"; "National Medal of Science," *Engineering and Science* [Cal Tech], March 1963: 16–17.

9. Clearly, Kármán was in failing health at the time he received the medal from Kennedy. The day after the ceremony, just before leaving for Paris, he made a will in the presence of Andrew Haley. Kármán's will (see chap. 4, n. 1); Walkowicz, "Kármán's Contributions," 67 (see chap. 6, n. 9); Wattendorf and Malina, "Kármán," 6 (see chap. 1, n. 3); Malina, "Kármán," 241 (see chap. 5, n. 18); "Space Scientist von Kármán, 81," *Washington Post,* May 8, 1963; "Von Kármán, Missilery Pioneer, Dies," Pasadena *Star News,* May 7, 1963; Kármán, *Wind and Beyond,* 12; "Dr. Von Kármán, Physicist, 81, Dies" New York *Times,* May 8, 1963; interview, Sears with Gorn, February 6, 1990.

10. Kármán, *Wind and Beyond,* 12; unknown correspondent to Lt. Gen. James Ferguson, May 6, 1963, USAFA; Ferguson to Vice-Commander-in-Chief, U.S. Air Forces in Europe, May 7, 1963, USAFA; Gen. William F. McKee to Schriever, May 7, 1963, USAFA; Schriever to McKee, May 8, 1963, USAFA; A. Y. Kent to all personnel, Headquarters USAF, May 8, 1963, USAFA; Lt. Col. Robert Hartwig to Military Air Transport Service, May 8, 1963, USAFA; Stever to Blockhouse Signal Office, Paris, May 7, 1963, USAFA; Proposed Statements [on Kármán's death] by Secretary of the Air Force Zuckert, Chief of Staff General LeMay, and Lieutenant General Ferguson, n.d., USAFA; "Von Kármán, 'Space Age's Father,' Dies," Los Angeles *Times,* May 8, 1963; "Space Pioneer Honored," Pasadena *Star News,* May 8, 1963; Col. Clyde D. Gasser to members of the Scientific Advisory Board, May 8, 1963, USAFA; Ferguson to Lt. Gen. Richard M. Montgomery, May 22, 1963, USAFA.

11. The author visited Kármán's resting place at Hollywood Cemetery in December 1988 and 1989. Kármán, *Wind and Beyond,* 12–13; "Space Pioneer Buried," Pasadena *Star News,* May 15, 1963; Gasser to SAB members, May 8, 1963; Ferguson to Montgomery, May 22, 1963.

12. Kármán's will, "Inventory and Appraisement" (see chap. 4, n. 1).

13. Sears, "Some Recollections," 8 (see chap. 1, n. 1); interview, Sears with Gorn.

14. Sears, "Some Recollections," 8; Wattendorf and Malina, "Kármán," 82 (see chap. 1, n. 3); Millikan, "Kármán—His American Period," 617 (see chap. 1, n. 1); Dryden, "Contributions," 17 (see chap 1, n. 15); interview, Pickering with Gorn, December 27, 1989; on-line computer run of all entries in *Dissertations Abstracts,* 1861–1988 (subject: Theodore von Kármán).

15. Sears, "Some Recollections," 5–6; Taylor, "Memories of Kármán," 479 (see chap. 1, n. 15).

16. Interview, Sears with Gorn.

17. Interview, Stewart with Gorn, December 29, 1989; Dryden, "Theodore von Kármán," 345–46 (see chap. 1, n. 18).

# Essay on Sources

Readers interested in learning more about the career of Theodore von Kármán might expect to find rich veins of archival ore, the natural by-product of a long and productive life. They will be disappointed. His fast pace and personal magnetism compelled Kármán to communicate vital matters not by the formal but by the informal word. Busy from morning to night as a teacher, practicing scientist, adviser to government and industry, aeronautics organizer, and tireless party-goer, he preferred to dispatch crucial business with a quiet talk over cocktails or a note scratched on a dinner receipt. This style of work relegated technical detail to follow-up letters, resulting in a correspondence steeped in scientific discussion but often lacking in personal reflection.

Yet, Kármán's motives and attitudes can still be discerned. Some revealing letters and a vast array of useful working papers exist in various manuscript collections. There is also a small but important oral record. Because of his vivid personality and preeminence in aviation circles, many associates memorialized him. The Hungarian also left a large collection of his own thoughts in published literature, lectures, and speeches. Finally, a number of scholars and popular authors have written books and articles on Kármán's immense contributions to aeronautics and astronautics.

## UNPUBLISHED PRIMARY SOURCES

The archives of the California Institute of Technology serve as the principal repository of Kármán papers, containing those files and photographs in his possession at the time of his death. They were transferred to the archives in 1968 and over the next twelve years some 145,000 pages were inventoried, arranged, and (with the support of the Smithsonian National Air and Space Museum) microfiched. *The Theodore von Kármán Collection at the California Institute of Technology* (Pasadena: Cal

Tech Archives, 1981), edited by archivist Judith R. Goldstein and assistant Carolyn Kopp, is a systematic finding aid to his correspondence, scientific notes, business records, lectures, articles, and illustrative materials. Although organized meticulously, the documents concentrate on Kármán's technical and administrative achievements, rather than his inner life. Nonetheless, much can be inferred from the astonishing diversity of personalities and projects which absorbed his mind.

Although less comprehensive than the holdings at Cal Tech, a number of other collections shed light on particular aspects of Kármán's career. The Jet Propulsion Laboratory archives in Pasadena, California, maintains fine manuscripts on the rocketry experiments supervised by Kármán during the 1930s, when he directed GALCIT. There are also valuable items on the founding of JPL, the origins of the Aerojet Engineering Corporation, and the GALCIT rocket contracts with the U.S. Army and Navy during World War II. The best overall collection of wartime materials is in the Office of Air Force History, located at Bolling Air Force Base, Washington, D.C. Documents there explain his involvement with Commanding General of the Army Air Forces Henry H. Arnold and reveal the scientist's role in *Toward New Horizons,* the famous aeronautics forecast undertaken in 1944 and 1945.

Four other institutions supplied primary sources for this book. The U.S. Air Force Scientific Advisory Board offices in the Pentagon, Arlington, Virginia, house valuable documents relating to the board's establishment and turbulent early period. Lacking the permanence of a true archive, however, these papers are perishable. Kármán's initial reluctance (but ultimate acquiescence) in revisiting *Toward New Horizons* may be traced in files held at the National Academy of Sciences, Washington, D.C. Related to the Woods Hole Summer Studies of 1957 and 1958, they are rich in content and open a window into one of the Boss's last major projects. For those interested in the technical details of Kármán's two great reports on the future of aviation science, the Office of History at Air Force Materiel Command, Dayton, Ohio, maintains the complete, original, multivolume editions both of *Toward New Horizons,* and the Woods Hole Summer Studies. Finally, the Special Collections Branch of the U.S. Air Force Academy Library, Colorado Springs, Colorado, contains a small but impressive group of manuscripts centered on Kármán's later years. Through these pages, his career as elder statesman of aeronautics may be understood.

From these last years, two oral interviews survive, each recorded early in 1960. One, conducted by Shirley Thomas, is available in audio form at the Eli Lilly Library at the University of Indiana. The other, with Donald Shaughnessy, is a transcription on file at the U.S. Air Force Historical Research Center, Maxwell Air Force Base, Alabama. Neither are long, but both are precious sources for learning his inner world. Sadly, the opportunity to speak personally to Kármán's colleagues has nearly passed. Still, Dr. William Pickering, the long-time director of the JPL, reflected quietly on the Boss in the mid-1940s. Another distinguished associate, Dr. H. Guyford Stever, a former White House science adviser, described on tape the wartime sojourns to Europe on behalf of General Arnold. Two of Kármán's eminent students—doctors William R. Sears and Homer J. Stewart—spoke eloquently and at length about their mentor as teacher, scientist, friend, and institution-maker. Their insights cannot be overvalued. Shirley Thomas made a few telling observations about her 1960 encounter with the aged scientist. Last, but certainly not least, Stanley Brozek, who purchased Kármán's Marengo Avenue home over twenty years ago, related what he knew about the domestic habits of the former owner.

PUBLISHED PRIMARY SOURCES

Memorials honoring Theodore von Kármán, which appeared in scholarly periodicals after his death, comprise a small but surprisingly informative literature. The students and colleagues who wrote these recollections knew him intimately, some for as long as forty years. William Sears is perhaps the most sensitive interpreter of Kármán's temperament, pedagogical techniques, and scientific contributions. He paid tribute to his professor in several journals, but his best work, "Recollections of Theodore von Kármán" appeared in *Theodore von Kármán, 1881-1963, In Memoriam* (Philadelphia: Society for Practical and Applied Mathematics, 1965). Frank J. Malina wrote several highly informative pieces on Kármán and rocketry. With another pupil, Frank Wattendorf, he remembered the Hungarian in a perceptive essay entitled "Theodore von Kármán, 1881-1963" (*Astronautica Acta,* 1964). W. D. Rannie's article of the same name in Cal Tech's *Engineering and Science* (June 1963) is a less balanced account. It is much like that of another student, Ernest E. Sechler, whose "Salute to Todor" (*Engineering and Science,* May 1956) celebrated Kármán on his seventy-fifth birthday.

The most prolific memorialist was not a pupil, but Kármán's eminent friend Hugh Dryden. Among Dryden's many pieces, "Theodore von Kármán, 1881-1963" (*Biographical Memoirs of the National Academy of Sciences,* 1965) is the most complete reminiscence, appended to which is a comprehensive list of the Boss's publications. In the same vein are the many tributes by GALCIT director Clark B. Millikan, in particular, "Theodore von Kármán—His American Period" (*Journal of the Royal Aeronautical Society,* 1963). Two English scientists left incisive and thoughtful observations on Kármán's career: S. Goldstein's "Theodore von Kármán, 1881-1963" (*Biographical Memoirs of the Fellows of the Royal Society,* 1966) and Geoffrey I. Taylor's "Memoirs of Kármán" (*Journal of Fluid Mechanics,* 1963).

Much of the life's work eulogized in these memorials may be read in Kármán's own words. During the six decades between 1902 and 1963, he sent to press an astonishing four books and over two hundred articles, reports, and published lectures. His longer works became essential textbooks in aerodynamic theory; for example, with Shih I. Pai, *From Low Speed Aerodynamics to Astronautics* (New York: Macmillan, 1963). More important, the four-volume *Collected Works of Theodore von Kármán* (London: Butterworth, 1956) provides an excellent survey of his research pursuits. Clearly, it shows a man of catholic tastes. At 21 years of age he published his first paper, "The Motion of a Heavy Rod Supported on Its Rounded End by a Horizontal Plate" (Budapest: Mathematical Society, 1902). It betrayed no interest in flight. In 1910, he pondered related questions in "What Determines the Stress-Strain Behavior of Matter?" (*Journal of the Society of Hungarian Engineers and Architects* [Budapest], 1910). But before, and then after World War I, his mind became consumed with the fundamentals of aerodynamics. During the 1920s and 1930s a torrent of articles poured forth, culminating in such seminal papers as "Turbulence and Skin Friction" (*Journal of the Aeronautical Sciences,* 1934), and "The Fundamentals of the Statistical Theory of Turbulence" (*Journal of the Aeronautical Sciences,* 1937). During World War II, he added to his repertoire with rocketry; for instance, "Comparative Study of Jet Propulsion Systems as Applied to Missiles and Transonic Aircraft" (JPL Memorandum-2, 1944). Later in life Kármán retained his previous interests, but added others, such as aerothermochemistry, and wrote increasingly for the popular media on institutional issues in aeronautics. He contributed a series to *Interavia* on such subjects as collectivized science ("From Newton's Notebook to Mammoth Research Organizations," 1952) and the wisdom of pursuing ever-increased aircraft speed ("Faster, Higher, Hotter," 1956).

Naturally, the most accessible of Kármán's works is his memoir, *The Wind and Beyond: Theodore von Kármán, Pioneer in Aviation and Pathfinder in Space* (Boston: Little, Brown, 1967). Journalist Lee Edson actually wrote the book, based on interviews with the Boss from the late 1950s until his death. Although the book was still unfinished in May 1963, Edson plunged ahead (with U. S. Air Force assistance) to research the last chapters of Kármán's life. *The Wind and Beyond* is immensely valuable for understanding the general contours of an extraordinarily complex career, but it sometimes scrambles the order of events, reports contextual facts incorrectly, and exaggerates successes. Although it includes no source notes or bibliography, *The Wind and Beyond* deserves a special place in aviation literature because it broadly reflects the mind of a crucial personality. Since it lacks either the scholarship of biography or the immediacy of autobiography, it must be used with care.

SECONDARY SOURCES

Works about Kármán by scholars and authors are few in number and vary widely in quality. Paul A. Hanle's pioneering and inventive book, *Bringing Aerodynamics to America* (Cambridge: MIT, 1982), raised to a new level the research on the Hungarian. It is the first study to dispassionately assess Kármán's international influence on aeronautics, skillfully placing him in the European tradition of science and engineering and tracing his difficult passage to the United States. At the opposite end of the spectrum, Daniel S. Halacy's *Father of Supersonic Flight: Theodore von Kármán* (New York: Julian Messner, 1965) is a colorful tale written for the young adult. The dialogue in the story appears to be fictional, although the sequence of events is basically correct. Two other studies treat Kármán's activities at some length and both involve his later years. In *The AGARD History, 1952-1968* and *The AGARD History, 1952-1987* (Paris: AGARD, 1969 and 1988) the respective editors—Frank L. Wattendorf and Trevor Sharp—describe his role in founding and nurturing this vital institution. The 1988 version also lists all of his publications.

A number of studies shed light on the world in which Kármán operated. Richard P. Hallion's excellent *Legacy of Flight: The Guggenheim Contribution to American Aviation* (Seattle: University of Washington Press, 1977) gracefully unwinds the complicated skein of Guggenheim generosity. It shows clearly GALCIT's important role in an ambitious national program to encourage aeronautics. The origins of the Jet Propulsion Laboratory, one of Kármán's most successful enterprises, is deftly covered in Clayton R. Koppes's *JPL and the American Space Program: A History of the Jet Propulsion Laboratory* (New Haven: Yale University Press, 1982). Robert H. Goddard's viewpoint in the quest for rocketry is available in a reliable work by Milton Lehman entitled *Robert H. Goddard: Pioneer of Space Research*, available recently in reprint (New York: Da Capo, 1988). Kármán's postwar years with the U.S. Air Force are treated ably in Thomas Sturm's *The USAF Scientific Advisory Board: Its First Twenty Years, 1944-1964* (rpt.: Washington, D.C.: Office of Air Force History, 1986). The broader question of the relationship between air power and technology is explained masterfully in Nick A. Komons's *Science and the Air Force: A History of the Air Force Office of Scientific Research* (Arlington, Va.: Office of Aerospace Research, 1966). Finally, the influence of the NACA on basic and applied aeronautical research may be read in two excellent books in the NASA History series: Alex Roland's *Model Research: The National Advisory Committee for Aeronautics, 1915-1958* (Washington, D.C.: NASA, 1985); and James R. Hansen's *Engineer in Charge: A History of the Langley Aeronautical Laboratory, 1917-1958* (Washington, D.C.: NASA, 1987).

A number of articles summarize all, or scrutinize part, of Kármán's career. The most complete and well researched is R. Cargill Hall's wonderfully written piece, "Shaping the Course of Aeronautics, Rocketry, and Astronautics: Theodore von Kármán, 1881-1963," in the *Journal of the Astronautical Sciences* (October-December 1978). A shorter version of Hall's work was published in the December 1981 issue of *Aerospace Historian*. Less scholarly than Hall but important because of the personal interview on which it is based, *Men of Space* by Shirley Thomas (Philadelphia: Chilton, 1960-1968) includes in the first of eight volumes a useful essay on Kármán. Lee Edson also rooted "He Tamed the Wind" (*Saturday Evening Post*, August 3, 1957) in discussions with the Boss, and much of his long reportage reveals original material. Theodore F. Walkowicz, who worked intimately with Kármán on the U.S. Air Force Scientific Advisory Board, reflected on this period in "Von Kármán's Singular Contributions to U.S. Aerospace Power" (*Air Force Magazine*, May 1981). Less instructive and more adulatory is "Dr. Theodore von Kármán, Gemütlicher Genius of Aeronautics" (*Air Force Magazine*, October 1957) by Robert Cahn. Insights on the scientist's early fascination with flight are described with customary vigor by Tom D. Crouch in his "Taking to the Air: Modern Aviation Got Its Lift from Vacuum Cleaners and Vortices" (*Science,* November 1984). Prior to the publication of *Model Research,* Alex Roland suggested the influence of national aviation policy on Kármán and other scientists in "The Impact of War upon Aeronautical Progress: The Experience of the NACA," in *Air Power and Warfare: Proceedings of the Eighth Military History Symposium,* transcribed from a meeting held at the U.S. Air Force Academy (Washington, D.C.: Office of Air Force History and the U.S. Air Force Academy, 1979).

# Index